101 Herbs

Descriptions   Remedies   Recipes

with
Stories and Essays

Marcia Neely

**Artwork by
Doug Pederson**

Honey & Herbs Press
Benson, MN

D1473308

Printed in the United States of America
ISBN 978-1-4243-3685-2

With special thanks to Matthew Wood,
herbalist and teacher,
who introduced me to the study of herbs
and provided
the fertile soil in which my
learning took root.

John Neely, my husband, helped remedy computer problems I faced, tolerated
my frustration with the same, and provided ideas and support. I deeply
appreciate his love and assistance. Nancy Overcott, a close friend whose
writing inspired mine, edited this manuscript and contributed to its readability.
I'm grateful for her friendship, inspiration, and expertise.

To my friends Sue Dyer, Sharon LaPoint, and Susan Zanin.

For more than ten years, we have met monthly at each other's homes for dinner and conversation. Their lives have inspired mine, their ideas and questions have stimulated thought and reflection, and their caring friendship has strengthened me.

Table of Contents

Essays and stories

Recipes and Herbal Preparations

101 Herbs
Stories and Essays

Introduction

This book began as an herbal, describing the herbs that grow wild or in the gardens at the Honey & Herbs farm near Benson, Minnesota.
I have planted, tended, harvested, and used the herbs that I've described.

As the book developed, I decided to incorporate stories and essays that I have written over the past fifteen years. They are not in any chronological order. In a sense, though, they provide a diary or memoir of my middle to later years, reflecting my enchantment with country living and the life forms in my environment and my disenchantment with many of society's institutions. The stories and essays are in sections scattered throughout the herbal.

The herbal is organized in alphabetical order using the English names of the herbs. The Latin names of the herbs follow the English names and are written in italics. The general characteristics of each herb are described, along with the medicinal value, growing patterns, and harvest suggestions. Also included are a number of culinary recipes and directions for making herbal preparations using some of the herbs described. The words of herbalists from centuries past provide a historical vision of many of the herbs, a view often supported by modern scientific study. Usually I use the word *tisane* to indicate a hot herbal infusion, commonly called an herbal tea. Technically, the word *tea* should be reserved for the leaves of the plant *Camelia sinensis*.

Traditional western herbalism, the approach of the herbal information in this book, is a blending of European and Native American traditions. An informative and interesting picture of 101 herbs is provided, but it is certainly not comprehensive. Hopefully this information will stimulate additional learning through researching other books, searching the internet, and growing, tasting, and using the herbs.

Many plants that most people would call "weeds" are medicinal herbs, such as stinging nettle, dandelion, burdock, red clover, and goldenrod. Although technically the word *herb* should be reserved for the herbaceous plants, those without woody stems, common plants such as the apple tree and cayenne pepper are also considered to be medicinal herbs and are included in this herbal.

Fundamental to any herbal approach is eating real food—chickens, pigs, and cattle that range on diverse farms; real butter or olive oil; vegetables that grow in healthy soil fertilized by nature; and eggs from free-range chickens that contain an abundance of omega 3 fatty acids as well as lecithin, which counteracts any negative effect of the cholesterol in the yolk. Herbal traditions include eating plenty of uncooked fruits and vegetables, herbs, and honey, to provide essential enzymes, which modern science has demonstrated are important for health and energy.

Plants evolved along with the rest of life forms. They produced substances to protect themselves from bacteria, viruses, and fungi and to keep predator insects and animals from eating too much of them. It is primarily these protective substances that we recognize as having medicinal value, although various minerals and vitamins within most herbs have healing value in their own right. Clearly, the plants we call "weeds" have tremendous capacity for survival.

Herbalism is grounded in the wisdom of the earth and always includes an intuitive aspect. It uses science, but not necessarily as its central feature. The difference between modern or allopathic medicine and the herbal approach is similar to that of corporate, technological, and engineered agriculture as contrasted with the truly organic or traditional, sustainable approach.

Some herbs have very specific actions—and as such are sometimes used similarly to a modern medicine. But, most herbs have many uses and act on the tissues in the body on a deeper level than do modern pharmaceuticals. Usually they act gently over a period of time, rather than immediately. Some work to assist the assimilation of foods by improving digestion. Others improve metabolism and enhance the elimination of toxins by stimulating the liver or kidneys. Herbs are used primarily to stimulate the body toward balance.

Culinary herbs, such as rosemary and thyme, are simply herbs for which we humans have developed a taste. Most of these are also medicinal herbs, having antibacterial, antiviral, and antifungal qualities in addition to aiding digestion. They likely were initially used for their digestive and antimicrobial action in the days before refrigeration. It was later that, due to their use as preservatives, we developed a taste for their pungency and aromatic qualities.

Most herbs are safe. Burdock root sandwiches were once common. Stinging nettle leaves can be cooked and eaten like spinach. Lambs quarter leaves can be added to your salads. Marshmallow, chamomile, lemon balm, hot pepper, apples, and many other herbs are often used as food. Most herbs are used to enhance health rather than to treat disease. However, when using anything as a medicine, caution is always recommended. Know an herb well before using it.

There is a lot of hyperbole about herbs, as there is about pharmaceutical medicines. And there are risks. The herb licorice, for instance, should not be used for persons with excessively high blood pressure. If you are taking anticoagulants or have cardiac arrhythmias, *Gingko biloba* should be used only with on-going evaluation. *Ephedra* (or *ma huang*) should be used only with extreme caution.

However, one should also compare the safety of herbs with the safety of pharmaceuticals, which cause upwards of one hundred thousand deaths a year in this country. Yet, when one person dies from a reaction to an herb it becomes a media story. Some call for more control of herbs. Knowledge is vital, but control and regulation do not guarantee either knowledge or safety. Regulation does guarantee increased costs, a diminution of the options available, and the making of health care, with its use of pharmaceuticals, into a monopoly similar to that of agribusiness, which has taken over control and distribution of much of the world's food.

"Medicines" we can grow in our own back yards threaten the established megabusinesses of health care, pharmaceuticals, and medical insurance.

I honor the earth. I see wisdom and mystery in all of life, and especially in the plants, wild creatures, and pets that I have written about in this book.

Marcia Neely

Agrimony

Agrimonia eupatoria
Perennial

Agrimony is an herb of antiquity, known to the ancient Egyptians. It helps improve liver and gallbladder function, as do most herbs with yellow/orange flowers. Agrimony also helps control symptoms of allergies that are worsened by tension and is used in tincture form for psoriasis, along with burdock, red clover, and yellow dock. As an astringent, agrimony helps control bleeding, so is helpful for small injuries. As an anti-inflammatory, it has been used to treat problems such as cystitis, colitis, and arthritic conditions. In addition, agrimony reportedly has anti-tumor activity. Perhaps best known is its use for emotional tension. Agrimony is an ideal herb to use for "torturedly cheerful" people to diminish the tension of holding emotions without release, as described by herbalist Matthew Wood. Wood further states it is useful for pain that causes breath holding and for "bad hair days." It helps reduce some types of hypertension, especially in people who feel caught in a bind. Finally, the leaves, fresh or as a tincture, can be used as a gargle for sore throats and mouth inflammation, helping to clear the voice for singers and public speakers.

The herbalist John Gerard writing in Olde English in 1633 said, "The decoction of the leaues of Egrimony is good for them that haue naughty liuers and for fuch as piffe bloud vpon the difeafes of the kidnies." (The decoction of the leaves of Agrimony is good for those that have naughty livers and for such as piss blood with diseases of the kidneys.)

Agrimony may be grown as a border or in a wildflower meadow. It will grow from seeds but takes many weeks to germinate. The plant grows one and one-half feet high, producing small yellow flowers in spikes that become burs before summer's end. It is not invasive, likes sun, and tolerates dry and alkaline conditions.

Harvest the leaves before flowering. Don't use as a tisane after flowering because the burs are sharp. It is best to use fresh leaves to make tinctures or to dry for tisanes, which are pleasant tasting.

Andrographis

Andrographis paniculata
Annual

In Scandinavia, andrographis is now the main herb used to fight the common cold and respiratory flu. However, the herb was known in ancient

1

times. Clinical trials show good effectiveness from andrographis and better immune enhancing activity than *Echinacea.* The herb helps battle viral and bacterial infections and prevent their reoccurrence. It also has adaptogenic properties, meaning it is tonic to several organs and systems, helping the body adapt to stress and improve resistance to disease. In addition, andrographis has shown anti-cancer effect, is considered a bitter tonic, expels intestinal parasites, and is highly antioxidant, which helps protect the liver.

Andrographis is an easy to grow annual native to India, South China, Vietnam, Malaysia, and Indonesia, but also grows well in Minnesota.

Use the flowers and leaves picked while flowering for tisane or tincture.

Angelica

Angelica archangelica
Biennial

Angelica is the ideal herb for women who feel hollow and sense that their lives are not actualized (Wood). It relaxes cold, stiff joints and is antiviral. It was reportedly revealed to a monk in a dream as a cure for the plague and was also used for typhoid fever. Angelica's hollow stems can be candied and used in confections and to flavor liquors and licorice. It is a remedy for colds, respiratory infections, flu, and arthritic conditions as well as for circulatory problems such as Buerger's disease. Angelica is said to open the imagination in those who are open to its magic. This herb may increase blood sugar, so diabetics should use it with caution and it should be used carefully or not at all by pregnant women.

Angelica is a bushy, aromatic biennial with large leaves and small white flowers that appear in large umbels, making for an attractive garden plant. It does well in shade or partial shade. The stems are hollow. It is native to northern and eastern Europe, Greenland, and Central Asia.

Gerard sayeth, "The root of garden Angelica is a fingular remedy againft poifon, and againft the plague, and all infections taken by euill and corrupt aire." (The root of garden Angelica is a singular remedy against poison, and against the plague and all infections taken by evil and corrupt air.)

2

The roots of angelica are the most medicinal, but the leaves and stalks have similar properties. The roots should be extracted in alcohol, rather than dried, because they are difficult to dry completely so they can turn rancid. The leaves and stalks can be dried. The flower buds and young stalks can be eaten raw in salads and are a good addition to stewed rhubarb and jams. The essential oil of angelica tastes similar to Benedictine and has been used to flavor candy, ice cream, liqueurs, and vodka.

Apple   *Malus species—Malus domesticata* (domesticated apple)

Deciduous tree

Apples contain potassium, iron, beta carotene, and magnesium. Malic and tartaric acids in apples neutralize the products of indigestion and assist digestion of fatty foods. Pectin in apples helps remove heavy metals, reduces cholesterol by decreasing the absorption of cholesterol and fat in the small intestine, slows the absorption of sugars and carbohydrates, increases energy efficiency, and slows the rise of blood sugar. The fiber improves the health of the intestine. A flavonol in apples promotes healthy heart functioning. *Apple pie isn't so unhealthy after all.* Apples and apple juice have also been used to dissolve gallstones, or make them smaller so they can pass when the gallbladder is stimulated with a quantity of olive oil.

The ancient apple likely originated in the Tien Shan Mountains in the border country between China and Kazakhstan and Kirghizia. The *Malus domesticata* species of trees has hundreds of varieties. Haralson and Honey Crisp, which are tart and sweet, and the very sweet Connell Red are some favorite varieties in Minnesota.

Apple ginger pie

Prepare your favorite crust. Place unbaked bottom crust in 9" deep pie plate.

Make filling:
4 pounds Haralson or other tart apples, peeled, cored, and sliced.
1/4 cup brown sugar
1/2 cup white sugar
2 tsp. powdered ginger
1/2 tsp. cinnamon
1/2 tsp. salt
3 T flour
1 T lemon juice

2 T butter

Put filling in bottom pie crust. Cut butter into small pieces and place on filling. Place top crust over filling, making sure there are slits to allow steam to escape. Bake at 400 degrees about 1 hour until the juice is bubbly.

Gerard wrote, "The pulpe of the rofted apples, in number foure or fiue … mixed in a wine quart of water, laboured together vntill it come to be as apples and ale, which we call Lambes Wooll, and the whole quart drunke laft at night, within the fpace of an houre, doth in one night cure thofe that piffe by droppes with great anguifh." (The pulp of the roasted apples, in number four or five, mixed in a wine quart of water, labored together until it comes to be as apples and ale, and the whole quart drunk last at night, within the space of an hour, doth in one night cure those that piss by drops in great anguish.). *I imagine Gerard's concoction produced an alcoholic cider.*

The fruit is eaten fresh, dried, or pressed into juice or cider—sweet or hard.

Arnica
Arnica montana and *chamissonis*
Short lived perennial

Arnica is generally used externally for bruises, burns, and inflammations. An infused oil is made by soaking the flowers and/or roots in safflower or olive oil. Arnica, taken internally, has reputed use for heart complaints, but in the United States it is deemed unsafe for internal usage unless in homeopathic doses or under the direction of a very qualified practitioner. Homeopathic arnica is frequently used for post-accident trauma.

Arnica is a short perennial, usually less than one foot high with yellow daisy-like flowers. It grows wild in much of the sub-arctic areas of the northern hemisphere.

Harvest the flowers when fully opened. The flowers contain more *arnican* than the root, but the root has tannins that the flowers don't have. Soak fresh or dried parts in olive oil to make an infused oil or apply a poultice of an infusion of fresh flowers. Arnica occasionally causes contact dermatitis when applied externally, so it is best to avoid long-term use. Tinctures of arnica can be used in a gargle or mouthwash for throat and mouth inflammation, but should not be swallowed.

Ashwagandha
Withania somnifera
Annual in the Midwest; perennial in southern climes

Sometimes called "Indian ginseng," ashwagandha is the primary strengthening tonic in Ayurvedic medicine. It is used for debility, nervous exhaustion, geriatric complaints, insomnia, impotence, infertility, joint and nerve pains, and just about anything else. The fruits and leaves are used to stimulate contractions in prolonged labor and retained placenta. Externally, it is used on wounds, stings, and burns.

This is a perennial evergreen shrub in southern climates. In Minnesota, ashwagandha grows as an annual. Tiny green-yellow flowers grow in clusters with orange-red berries appearing in the fall.

The roots are the most medicinal part of the plant, although the leaves and flowers can be used. Use the roots for decoction and the aerial parts for tincture. In Ayruvedic medicine ashwagandha is usually decocted in milk.

Baikal skullcap

Scutellaria baicalensis
Perennial

Baikal skullcap is used for pain and inflammation. It is also a nervine for anxiety and a remedy for hypertension and elevated cholesterol. It inhibits histamine so helps diminish allergic symptoms. It is antibacterial, anti-spasmotic, and is diuretic with anti-toxic properties. It is especially helpful for autoimmune disorders and also useful for chronic hepatitis, urinary tract infections, and threatened miscarriage. Its astringent properties make it useful for hemorrhage, especially from the bowel or lungs.

Baikal skullcap is a spreading short bushy perennial, growing twelve to eighteen inches high with purple flower spikes. It makes an attractive flower garden border.

Use the root as a tincture or decoction.

Basil

Ocimum basilicum
Annual

The Greek word for basil means royal and basil is another herb that was known in antiquity. It is an uplifting herb that is useful for nervous exhaustion as well as for "down in the dumps" feelings, tension headaches, and insomnia. It helps neutralize past damage from drug use, especially marijuana use. In addition, basil lowers fevers, is antispasmotic, antibacterial, and anti-parasitic, and improves digestion. Chewing the leaves and applying them to an insect bite helps take away the sting. Basil is a remedy for some

Basil marinated tomatoes

1 cup olive oil
1/3 cup red wine vinegar
1/4 cup fresh parsley, chopped
3 T fresh basil (or 1 T dried)
1 T honey
1 tsp. salt
1/2 tsp. black pepper
1/2 tsp. dry mustard
1 clove fresh squeezed garlic
  or 1/2 tsp. garlic powder
1 medium sweet onion, thinly sliced
6 large tomatoes, thinly sliced

Mix the first 9 ingredients. Layer onions and tomatoes in a shallow dish, adding marinade between each layer. Refrigerate for several hours.

migraines as well. Flowers and leaves are tinctured for medicinal use and are distilled for essential oil.

Basil is a also a wonderful culinary herb, especially in pastas, marinara sauces, and other Italian dishes. The flavor of the leaves tends to increase when cooked. Fresh leaves are good in salads, adding a special pungency, and make a great dressing when chopped and blended with vinegar and oil. Make pesto by pounding or grinding basil leaves, pine nuts or other nuts, and mixing with olive oil and Parmesan cheese.

Basil grows well from seed in zone four, especially if set out as soon as the spring frosts are over. Although the plant can be started inside and transplanted later, it produces almost as early if planted directly in the garden. In more northerly zones, however, it is better to put out plants instead of direct seeding. Basil grows one to two feet high depending upon the variety. It grows well in well-drained soil and needs full sun and is an attractive border plant. Using some green and some purple-leaved varieties makes a beautiful contrast in a garden. Genovese basil is more full flavored than sweet basil.

Of basil, Gerard wrote, "The juice mixed with fine meale of parched barly, oyle of rofes and vinegar, is good againft inflammations and the ftinging of venomous beafts. The juice clenfeth away the dimmeneffe of the eyes and drieth vp the humour that falleth into them. The feede drunke is a remedie for melancholicke people, for thofe that are fhortwinded, and them that can hardly make water." (The juice mixed with fine meal of parched barley, oil of roses and vinegar, is good against inflammations and the stinging of venomous beasts. The juice cleans away the dimness of the eyes and dries up the humour that falls into them. The seed drunk is a remedy for melancholic people, for those that are short-winded, and those that can hardly make water.)

Harvest the leaves before flowering for cooking. Pinch back the flowers to keep the harvest going longer. For medicinal uses, use both leaves and flowers. Basil can be dried, but takes a long time, so is best done in a dehydrator at a temperature of 110-115 degrees. It is never as flavorful dried as fresh. For medicinal purposes, use either a tincture or tisane.

Bergamot, wild

Monarda fistulosa
Perennial

Monarda is a remedy for yeast infections, bladder pain, Meniere's syndrome (inner ear problem causing imbalance), and for tinnitus or ringing in the ears. Native Americans also used it for respiratory conditions such as colds and flu and, since it increases perspiration, it is a useful herb for infections. It is antibacterial and antifungal and has a deep restorative action on the nervous system and tissues. Native Americans made teas from the leaves, even though they usually used the roots and barks of plants, rather than the aerial parts.

Wild bergamot is perennial and native to Minnesota. It has relatively small purple flowers, similar to the larger showy flowers of cultivated *Monarda*. A similar species, *Monarda didyma*, is native to the eastern United States and has red flowers. *Monarda fistulosa* grows about four feet high. It grows best in well-drained soils and needs little watering. It tends to develop powdery mildew later in the season. Pruning right after flowering can help prevent this. *Monarda didyma* needs more water than does *fistulosa* and does well in some shade.

Wild bergamot grows well from seed in zones three through nine, but is often purchased as small plants. If using seeds, it is best to plant inside in early spring and plant out-of-doors when the weather warms.

Pick the flowers and leaves at the height of flowering. Dried, *Monarda* makes a great Earl-Grey-tea-like tisane. Wild bergamot is also often tinctured for medicinal use. As a culinary herb, *Monarda fistulosa* flowers and leaves can be added to vegetable and meat dishes to give a robust taste.

Black walnut

Juglans nigra
Deciduous tree

The outer casing of the nut of the black walnut is rich in fruit acids and minerals. It has been promoted as a significant anti-cancer agent. It is also a purgative for eliminating intestinal worms and parasites and is a general tonic cleanser. The bark has comparable uses, although using butternut bark that has similar properties, is less irritating and more soothing. Skin problems such as eczema, eyelid inflammation (blepharatis), and impetigo also respond to walnut hull and bark. Walnut is said to be good for those who are too much under the influence of other persons (Wood). Walnut also helps remove gallstones. The leaves can be used for skin conditions, but are not effective for parasites and cancer. A walnut cordial made from the unripe nuts is an old German remedy. Maria Treben, writing in *Health Through God's Pharmacy* described the process of making a cordial from the unripe nuts of a related species, *Juglans regia*: "20 unripe nuts picked in early summer are quartered, put in a bottle and one litre of rye whiskey is poured over them so that they are covered by 2-3 finger widths. The bottle is covered, placed in a sunny place and kept for 2-4 weeks. The liquid is strained and bottled. As a cleanser, 1 teaspoonful is taken. A cordial is made by using 2-3 cloves, a piece of cinnamon stick, a piece of vanilla pod, rind of ½ of an orange and 500 grams of sugar, boiled in ¼ litre water, cooled and strained." This was used to cleanse the stomach, liver and blood, strengthen weak stomachs, and improve foul intestines.

Black walnut grows as a deciduous tree twenty to thirty feet high. Other plants will not grow under a walnut tree.

Hulls are harvested in the fall. They can be either green or black and are best gathered when they readily fall away from the nut. Use them as a decoction or tincture. The bark is collected in the late winter and can also be used either in decoction or tincture. Leaves used in a tisane help treat inflamed gums and throats. Made into an infusion, the leaves are useful for cradle cap and can be wrapped directly on skin irritations as a poultice. For culinary use, eat the nuts either raw or roasted.

Blue vervain
Verbena hastata
Perennial

Blue vervain is an antispasmotic, especially for neck tension. It is also a hormone regulator and an adjunct remedy with other herbs for menopausal symptoms, including hot flashes. It is best for idealistic people who feel driven and find fault with self and others (Wood, who references Dr. Bach). Additional uses are for swollen glands and impotence. *Verbena hastata* helps relieve sprains or strains of muscles due to hyperextension. It is considered an alterative, especially for the liver and lungs.

Blue vervain is a native prairie plant, not invasive, growing about four feet high with erect purple flower spikes. Native Americans had a tradition of giving milk and honey to the plant in exchange for its flowers and roots.

The root is used as a decoction or tincture. The flowering tops, gathered at the height of flowering, are used fresh to make a tincture or are dried for a tisane. It is best to take over a long time to produce long-term healing.

Boneset
Eupatorium perfoliatum
Perennial

Boneset is a remedy for intermittent and deep aching ("bone breaking") fever. It relieves aches of respiratory flu, stimulates the immune system, relieves congestion, and brings on a sweat, which relieves fever. It has also been used for preventing acid reflux. According to herbalist Halsey Brandt from Bisbee, Arizona, it also helps to prevent osteoporosis and recalcify bones by increasing the circulation to the periosteum.

Boneset is a native prairie bushy perennial growing two to three feet high with white flowers. It is not invasive.

Tincture the fresh flowers and leaves picked while flowering. The flowers and leaves can also be dried and used as a bitter tisane.

Borage
Borago officinalis
Self-seeding annual

Called the "herb of gladness," borage was noted for uplifting the spirits as well as bestowing courage. The flowers were used in wine to "maketh men merrie." This herb is used primarily today for the production of gamma linoleic acid (GLA), a fatty acid that is essential for hormonal regulation. The leaves and flowers stimulate adrenal function, promote lactation, and are slightly diuretic and expectorant. They have been used for muscular aches and mild feverish illnesses. The leaves help diminish the side effects of steroid treatment and, juiced, are used for depression and grief. The juice has also been used for ringworm. The essential oil extracted from the seeds helps treat eczema, regulate menstruation, and relieve irritable bowel syndrome.

Borage is sometimes called "star flower" because it produces beautiful small blue flowers, sometimes tinged with pink, in the shape of stars. It grows easily from seed and self seeds readily, so can be invasive. The plant has large downy leaves and by fall, its sprawling stems often need staking to prevent an unkempt look. The flowers attract honey bees. The flowers and leaves are edible, but the flower wilts soon after picking.

The leaves are harvested throughout the growing season for infusion and tincture or for fresh juice. They taste similar to cucumber and are sometimes added to salads. The seeds are used primarily for essential oil production. The flowers can be used to make a syrup for congestion. Frozen in ice cubes, the flowers make an interesting addition to wine or summer drinks.

Burdock   *Arctium lappa* and *Arctium minus*

Perennial

Burdock is described as an alterative, cleansing the liver and kidneys and ridding the system of toxic waste products, including heavy metals. It is also used for uterine prolapse and to reduce swollen prostate glands. The seeds act on the kidney and help to reduce blood cholesterol, while the root has more action on the liver. This is an important herb to consider for psoriasis and other disorders that erupt on the skin, showing internal imbalance and toxicity. The root acts more slowly than the seeds and is best used over time for chronic conditions. It is said that burdock helps deal with worries about the unknown and provides faith to move in new directions. Burdock is suited for people who retain fluid, yet look dry. It aids the body in the production of cortisol and other hormones, so is useful for inflammatory conditions and hormonal imbalances.

This common herb with huge leaves and large burs that stick to the clothing in the fall is well established in North America, but is native to Europe and Asia, not the United States. It grows extremely easily anywhere that the soil is open for the seeds in the burs to plant themselves. This is not something you want to grow in your garden; you can find it almost anywhere in the wild. Burdock is biennial, but obviously self seeds easily, so you'll find first and second year plants growing side by side.

The roots should be harvested at the end of the first season and either preserved in alcohol or dried soon after harvest. Grinding the seed heads in a coffee mill will help separate seeds from burs. Little splinters cling to the seeds, so fresh seeds should not be chewed. Prepare a decoction or tincture of the roots or seeds, making sure to strain the seed tincture well. The young roots can also be eaten fresh in salads, cooked like carrots, or added to stir fries. The stalks of the young plants are tasty when eaten like celery.

Butterfly weed (pleurisy root)   *Asclepias tuberosa*

Perennial

This herb is antispasmotic, diaphoretic (opening the pores of the skin), expectorant, purgative, and tonic. It subdues inflammation in the lungs and is among the best herbal expectorants, useful especially when lung conditions hang on for weeks or months. Wood also describes its use as a lubricant for joints with bursitis and arthritis and other conditions with adhesions. Generally, small doses should be used. Larger doses are emetic and strongly purgative. Named after the Greek god of medicine, Asklepios, the *tuberosa* species of *Asclepias* is native to the eastern and southern United States. It was used by Native Americans for centuries prior to the invasion of the Europeans. It is not suited for pregnant women.

This perennial plant grows one to two feet high and has yellow-orange flowers in clusters. It prefers some shade and a slightly acid soil, rather than the alkaline condition at Honey & Herbs.

The roots are dug in the fall for syrups, ointments, tinctures, or decoctions.

Butterbur

Petasites hybridus
Perennial

Butterbur reduces the risk of migraine headaches and helps relieve asthma and chronic bronchitis. It also makes a mucus reducing cough syrup. Butterbur was one of the treatments for plague. It treats infection in part by increasing perspiration and reducing fever. It is a heart stimulant, a cardiac tonic, and a diuretic. For acute asthma attacks, it is best used as a decoction in warm wine. The dose should be repeated frequently. As a tincture, butterbur is good for severe neuralgia in the small of the back. The large leaves are used as wraps for poultices, but also can be placed directly on burns, ulcers, and wounds.

Butterbur has large leaves like rhubarb and has a stocky, creeping root. It grows about three feet high and prefers wet locations and semi-shade. It is a good bee flower, producing one of the first emerging spring blooms in a mushroom-like head of tiny purple/rose flowers. The leaves come later.

Gerard says, "The roots of Butterburre ftamped with ale, and giveth to drinke in peftilence and burning feuers mightily cooleth and abateth the heate thereof. … The fame kills worms in the belly; it provoketh vrine and brings downe the monthly termes." (The roots of butterbur stamped with ale and given to drink in pestilence and burning fevers mightily cool and abate the heat thereof. The same kills worms in the belly and brings down the menses.)

Harvest the root for decoction or tincture.

Calamus (sweet flag)

Ascorus calamus
Perennial

It is said that Moses was commanded to use calamus as an ointment, but it is possible this referred to a different plant. Calamus is an antihistamine that also aids mental focus. It reduces stomach hyperacidity, reduces gas and bloating, and assists in the treatment of all disorders of the gastrointestinal tract, including liver, gallbladder, spleen, and pancreas. Treben said that extremely thin people should drink calamus root tea. She indicated that calamus improves the appetite, helps in kidney disorders, and cleanses the whole system. Treben also encouraged the use of warm calamus baths for chilblains and frostbite. (Steep the roots overnight in cool water; then boil. When cooled to warm, bathe the affected parts for twenty minutes.) Calamus may also help smokers give up the habit.

A reed-like perennial plant, calamus likes wet growing conditions. Its essential oil is bitter, pungent, and aromatic.

In addition to various other virtues, Gerard stated, "It is of great effect, put in broth or taken in fumes to provoke women's natural accidents." It would seem, then, that it is clearly best not to use this herb during pregnancy.

Dig the rhizomes in fall or early spring to make a tincture or decoction.

Calendula

Calendula officinalis
Self-seeding annual

Calendula hand therapy

Pick fresh calendula flowers. Remove the petals and put them in a glass jar. Cover the petals with olive oil, just filling so the petals are covered. Soak in bright sun for 7-10 days—or slowly bring to just below a simmer in a stainless steel pan. Heat for 30 minutes; then allow to cool. Strain. Discard the petals into your compost.

Add 2-3 drops of tincture of benzoin or a pinch of ground benzoin (as a preservative). Mix into the oil. Store or use immediately to make an ointment as follows:

10 oz. calendula oil
1 oz. vitamin E oil
5 oz. shea butter
1 T honey
1/2 oz. beeswax

Gently heat above together until the beeswax melts. Immediately pour into containers and cover.

Calendula grows in the sun and is good for places where the sun doesn't shine—in the lymph nodes. It stimulates good lymphatic drainage throughout the body. It is an immune system tonic and may even help the body rid itself of cancer. Used externally as salve or oil, it helps the skin heal without scarring and is often effective against athlete's foot. Treben touted it's usefulness in making strawberry marks and age spots disappear and even recommended it for herpes and non-healing potentially cancerous sores.

Calendula is sometimes called pot marigold. Its orange and yellow flowers are similar to a simple marigold. Some varieties have double flowers, but most are single.

It grows in zones three through nine in sunny conditions, but tolerates some shade. It should have good air circulation, so shouldn't be planted too thickly. Calendula grows well from seed started indoors or seeded directly. It also self seeds, so although it grows as an annual, you will usually find it growing the following year. Old blossoms should be pinched off to provide the best bloom. Calendula grows one to two feet high.

Harvest the whole flower of calendula, but pluck the petals, which are the only parts used medicinally. They can be dried for use in oils, ointments, and tisanes. Preserve the petals fresh in a tincture or preserve them in vinegar for use in salad dressings. Soaking the fresh petals in oil, leaving in the sun for a week or so, or gently heating, creates a more medicinal salve than dried petals. Dried flowers serve as a substitute for saffron in recipes.

Tincture fresh flower petals and dry them for tisanes. Also soak fresh, preferably, or dried petals in olive oil to make salves or ointments.

Catnip
Nepata cataria
Perennial

Internally, catnip is used for feverish illnesses, insomnia, nervous indigestion, anxiety, mild sedation, and digestive related headaches. It has also been used to comfort babies with colic and to help them sleep. It lowers fevers, increases perspiration, and relieves spasms. Used in pillows, dried catnip provides a pleasant minty aroma with a relaxing effect, even though it has a stimulant effect on many cats.

Catnip is often thought of as a weed, but makes a nice mint-tasting tea. It is native to Europe, southwest and central Asia, and, since being introduced, has become prevalent throughout much of the United States. It grows a couple of feet high and has purple flowers that bloom in mid-summer. It can be cut back hard for a second harvest. It grows in well drained, but moist soil in sun to partial shade. The leaves provide a natural repellent for cabbage worms, aphids, flea beetles, cucumber beetles, and squash beetles, so it's not a bad idea to let some of it grow in your vegetable garden.

Gerard commented on several virtues of catnip

13

similar to that expressed above. Referring to what today are called sitz baths, he added, "It is vfed in baths and decoctions for women to fit over to bring down their fickneffe and to make them fruitfull." (It is used in baths and decoctions for women to sit over to bring down their sickness and to make them fruitful.)

Harvest the aerial parts when in bloom for tisane or tincture or to dry for stuffing pillows.

Cayenne   *Capsicum annuum*
Annual

The fruit of cayenne (the hot pepper) is a stimulant for the whole body. It increases blood flow, tones the nervous system, relieves indigestion, and stimulates action. It may ease the pain of shingles and migraines. Although it may seem counter-intuitive, cayenne helps heal the mucosa of the stomach and intestine. It also encourages sweating and is antibacterial, so is good for infections. Mexican and South American cultures have used it in cooking and medicine for centuries. Cayenne has an immediate effect upon circulation and is recommended for use during a heart attack by applying a pinch of ground dried pepper on the tongue. Wooster Beach, an early twentieth century physician who combined herbal and "regular" medical approaches, discussed cayenne as an equalizer of circulation, believing that burdens are placed upon the heart when there is weakness or inequality in parts of the circulatory system.

Cayenne is especially helpful to people who have a purplish red coloring to the face and for those who are nostalgic, believing that life was better in the past, according to herbalist Matthew Wood. Cayenne is also helpful for persons whose extremities are cold and for that purpose is best used as a cold infusion sipped throughout the day. Finally, it can be used as a first aid treatment for cardiac problems and for wounds when medical care is not immediately available. For severe injuries exposing the internal organs, sprinkle ground cayenne directly on the viscera. Cayenne is antiseptic and antihemmorhagic, helping to stop bleeding.

Cayenne pepper grows as a vegetable garden plant and likes full sun and a lot of heat. The plant reaches one to one and one-half feet tall. The peppers are produced in mid to late summer.

Best harvested when the pepper turns fully red, the pepper can be used fresh in cooking or dried and powdered for use in food or for infusions.

Facing Death

This first story, written years ago, depicts a segment of my life as I cared for our son, JW, who had been diagnosed with primary pulmonary hypertension at age fifteen and had subsequently undergone a heart and double-lung transplant. Two years later, his transplanted lungs were failing.

"Do you and Dad think about me dying much?" JW asked after a foot-rub.

"Some."

"I rarely think about it," he said. "Maybe I don't accept it. Usually, the most distant thing I think about is going to bed at night." JW took a drink of tangerine juice. "I just pay attention to what is happening—the music, Lady barking. It's funny, even after my transplant, I came to take the basics of living—walking, breathing, and eating—for granted. Just after transplant, I noticed a flower in bloom, the little things. After a while, I stopped paying attention to the roses. Now they're important again. The soothing sound of your voice, the color of that pink pen..."

He had become more conscious of living things, too, not wanting to kill them, not even mosquitoes. He was glad to hear that I took some spiders to the basement after I destroyed their web in the pantry. That morning John had suggested taking him down to the river in the wheelchair to go fishing.

"I don't want to go fishing because I wouldn't be able to eat the fishies," JW responded. He may have been the only seventeen-year-old who dodged his car to avoid hitting a gopher or a frog on the road. It had even bothered him to mow the lawn at Animal Farm, the land where we were building our country home, because of the toads and snakes in the grass.

By late July, John and I rarely worked together at Animal Farm because we didn't want to leave JW alone for more than an hour or two. John spent most days building and I stayed with JW, whose occasional good days let him breathe comfortably at rest and even get out to his car. Usually, he struggled to breathe and used oxygen most the time. Even at rest, the strain in his face made it look as though he were hefting a bag of cement.

Occasionally at night he'd buzz for us. He had a pounding headache, or had vomited, or was almost unable to breathe. Sleep sometimes came after aspirin and a backrub.

Life was hard. Hard for all of us.

We still tried to enjoy the good days, and get through the tougher ones a day at a time, sometimes an hour at a time. On one of his good days, JW came out to our country property. We had a picnic and planted a pine sapling given to us by our friend Kerry who had recently succumbed to AIDS. We held a brief ceremony to honor Kerry's friendship.

Some nights later, John and I were tired and wanted to get to bed. JW had been in the bathroom for more than ten minutes. I wondered if he was okay, if he needed help, or was just sitting there contemplating.

I got up, walked to the bathroom, and called through the door, "I'm going to bed now."

"No, don't go. I need to talk," he commanded.

15

After he got back in bed, JW said, "I want you and Dad to tell me twenty minutes before you plan to go to bed, so I can go to the bathroom, get back to bed, and don't have to be scared that I can't get back."

I wanted to scream that I couldn't stand his dependence on me, couldn't stand having to plan everything in advance, couldn't stand his dying. A few days earlier when I came home from the grocery store, he'd said, "I counted the minutes until you got home." He so easily became dependent upon me and I so easily let that happen.

I ought to be able to support him without feeling anger. I want to keep caring, supporting, and loving, but my dark emotions surface, too. I need to honor the darkness as well as the light.

Shit. I don't know how to do any of this.

I told JW I'd let him know shortly before we went to bed, so he could get ready.

When we got into bed, I talked to John and he listened. He tenderly caressed my face and ran his fingers through my hair. "You don't have to be pleasant all the time, Marsh. You don't have to jump at JW's requests."

Talking helped some.

Occasionally, John stayed with JW in the evening and I went to visit my folks. It helped to get away for an hour or two.

Our daughter Misty was home for the evening and my folks had invited us for dinner. Misty drove JW over to their grandparents. When John and I arrived later, JW had been sitting in the car for half an hour. He sat there, motionless. He was looking at the ground.

"How are you?" I asked. *Dumb question.*

"Pretty crummy."

Mom called us to dinner. When everyone else was at the table, JW walked in. During the meal, he sat with his cap on. His face, as unmoving as the wall behind him, was parallel with the table. "Do you want some salad or potatoes?" Mom asked him.

Curtly, "No."

He ate a piece of ham and drank two glasses of punch.

I was glad he drank something.

We all talked about innocuous things during the meal, trying to be pleasant. There were some lulls in the conversation that felt uncomfortable.

Dinner was over and it was time to leave. Pops asked JW, "Do you want me to get the roller chair?"

"No." He continued to sit as we all looked nervously at each other and tried to figure out how to get him to the car.

A couple of minutes later, I stood up and walked out. John and Misty followed. JW stood up then, and walked to the car by himself.

The next morning, after he had been in the bathroom, he asked me if there was any medicine he could take to improve digestion. I told him that he was on one, that activity affected digestion, that little activity meant little digestive action. I asked him if he'd had a bowel movement recently.

"Not for a week."

"Oh, good for you," I said. "It obviously doesn't matter what I say. I told you to let me know if BMs were infrequent or hard or anything."

Then, he changed his story and said he'd had a BM two or three days ago.

"With my voice louder and firmer than usual I said, "That's normal for as little as you eat."

A little softer, I said, "It's sometimes hard to be around you, JW. I know it's hard for you, but when you just sit in a chair with your head down I want to walk away. You hardly do anything, which makes it hard for Dad and me and it's not helping you any."

"I try," he said.

I'm sure he does. God, all of us are trying and it's getting harder and harder.

I poured a cup of coffee. "I can't imagine how difficult this must be for you, but you can choose to be a Mensch or a Nebbish. You can make it tolerable—possibly even kind of good—or awful. You can involve yourself in conversations. You could even watch TV, or you can sit like a lump in the chair like Misty did when she was depressed."

"It's hard now because I feel like I'm walking on eggshells," he said.

Calmer now, I said with more empathy, "It feels to me like you're about to shatter, that you express hardly any emotion. There has to be rage, anger, awful feelings, and they're ready to shatter your body."

"I suppose," he said. Nothing further.

I left the kitchen to finish shampooing the carpet.

That night he asked me to rub his feet. I started massaging. I didn't say anything. Finally he started to talk, said he was angry at John and me, sometimes just for being able to escape.

"I'm sure that must be hard," I said.

"I don't know how to express what I'm feeling," he sighed.

"I believe that. Start by just acknowledging a feeling of the moment. As you begin to talk, the deeper feelings will surface."

He talked about how hard everything was, how mad he would get when he watched how easily other people did things. He talked about his fear of dying. After our time together, he was breathing easier. Then he asked John to make a copy of a computer game. He played computer games until we all got ready for bed. He didn't connect the oxygen as he settled into slumber.

In mid-August, JW and I visited Dr. Darrell Carter, a physician in Granite Falls. Two years earlier he had agreed to be available for any care JW needed locally. Until then, such care had been limited, since most of JW's care was provided at Abbott-Northwestern Hospital. But, we no longer wanted high tech evaluation or treatment. We needed a doctor to help manage the suffering—to palliate, not to cure.

The main reason for the visit was to give Dr. Darrell, as we called him, a better understanding of JW's condition. Tests to determine his oxygen saturation were done. At rest on oxygen, his oxygen saturation was ninety-four percent of normal. Walking without oxygen for about one minute brought the saturation in his blood down to the low sixties— just above where he would lose consciousness.

"Have you thought about what you want in terms of life support?" Dr. Darrell asked when talking with JW after the evaluation.

"We need to talk about it," JW said. "I'm not sure what all the possibilities are."

"I guess what I need to know is what you want me to do if oxygen deprivation makes you incoherent. Do you want us to put you on a ventilator? And how long do you want us to keep you on a vent if you don't respond?"

JW glanced at me. "I think I need to talk to Mom more about it," he said with a quivering voice. He looked down at the floor then. "Mostly I don't want to be kept alive if there isn't any hope."

Dr. Darrell was a doctor who was willing to assist with the process of dying and the relief of suffering. He prescribed morphine to ease JW's breathing during the especially bad times. I knew I had found someone who would be a partner to help me care for JW.

JW felt abandoned by the doctors and staff at Abbott-Northwestern who had been his life line until he was no longer the miracle transplant child, but a dying one. He knew that his future care was likely to be in Granite Falls. That visit to Dr. Darrell, however, stimulated a round of anxiety about the possible problems that might develop.

"I didn't realize there could be complications like losing my mind. I thought I would just get an infection and die," said JW, his voice shaky, his breaths coming too fast.

"I don't know whether I should go on life support. I don't know how long it makes sense to stay on it if I do. What if I just had a bronchial spasm and could get better if I was put on a vent?"

His eyes looked down at his bed. His voice was firmer. "I don't want to lose my mind. I don't want to live if I lose my mind."

By the end of August, JW was using oxygen all of the time. Tubing allowed him to get to the bathroom with a tether to the oxygen concentrator. In the bathroom, he connected directly to an oxygen tank, which gave him the higher concentration he needed after the effort of walking.

I could almost see the pounds dropping from his frail body. I supposed he ate an average of six hundred calories a day, most of them from some peach sauce I had canned. Most of the time, he stayed in bed. Even so, he had an increasingly difficult time breathing. His pulse was usually about one hundred and thirty beats a minute. His anxiety seemed to be making it all much harder. *If he could just relax ...*

He slept after meditation one night. The next night, meditation didn't do the trick. I thought that he spent most of his time concentrating on his body. He was full of fear. "It feels like I'm on a roller coaster," he said. "I'm a little kid and you and Dad are down below, and I'm so scared and can't get to you to help."

It felt like that to John and me too, that JW wanted us to solve his daily problems and keep him from dying. Of course we wanted to, but we couldn't stop his dying, couldn't even do much to ease the suffering.

"Do you think there's an inner wisdom inside you that you can tap into?" I asked.

"I don't know."

"I think the answers don't come from outside, but from inside, from deep within you," I suggested.

"I don't know."

Later that day, after our friend Orien visited and talked with JW, he seemed to be able to grasp the concept of inner wisdom a little bit. "Orien suggested that rather than being the little kid on the roller coaster, I am the roller coaster," said JW. "That helps."

JW was mad at John for being on the phone when he wanted to talk to him, mad at him for talking about the house we were building when he couldn't be a part of that.

JW was facing death, not just looking into her corners. "If I could just let go and know I'm going to die, I think I could feel kind of high and have a good time," he said.

"That's tapping your inner wisdom," I said. Yet, it was clear that JW was almost paralyzed with fear, that he didn't dare to let go. I wondered if I could, myself. *How*

18

terrifying the unknown is. We humans put ourselves through all sorts of torture to escape that step into the void or the mysterious.

I sometimes hated medical science for always putting the carrot out there—the medicine, the surgery, the new treatment that might help. I hated it for having ventilators available for prolonging life so that decisions had to be made about whether one wanted to live forever. Just dying had become too complicated.

When I'm ready to die, I hope I can sit by a tree and let my body shut down. Modern medicine, as criticized as it often is, is still the modern god, but I don't worship it.

I wondered when the balance would tip too far, when manipulation of human life would lead to such overpopulation that it would bring irreversible breakdown in both the social and ecological order. I wondered when too much technology would kill the human spirit.

"We usurp nature and divert her direction and cause imbalances we haven't begun to notice. We may cause the demise, not of an individual, but of a species, possibly all species," I said to Orien on one of his visits.

On another of his visits, I said, "It's so hard to watch him dying and so sad."

"The lesson to learn is that there is life and there is death, and neither is better than the other," Orien said.

That thought comforted me. It flickered through my mind later that day. *If I could integrate the idea that this physical existence is only a fragment of my existence, the point on which I'm currently shining the spotlight, then how much differently I could approach life.* I believed it intellectually, but that was not the same as knowing it.

Another wave of reality hit JW the next day when he got his schedule for school. He looked so sad and I asked him what he was thinking about.

"I know it isn't realistic to think about going to school, but I want to. It's so hard to know that I'm giving up my senior year."

That afternoon, he went out to the car, using portable oxygen, and rode with me to the drug store. When we returned, I watched his skinny body walking slowly back into the house. He looked more starved than the photos I had recently seen of people starving in Somalia. His feet pointed outward, for a bit of stability, I supposed. His torso bent forward over his quivering bird-like legs.

That night as John and I prepared to go upstairs to bed JW said, "Something just doesn't feel good. I hate the feeling. Something feels wrong."

As the night progressed, he listened to meditation tapes. He buzzed us at two o'clock, gasping, "I need help."

His breaths were short and fast, perhaps forty a minute. His head ached. He had dumped his medicine bottles out on his bed so he could use the container as a basin for vomit. He sobbed, "I just can hardly stand this."

I felt engulfed in thick black smoke, lacking any way to find him, to comfort him, to make him well. I looked up at the ceiling, trying to summon some energy or spirit. Finally, I mustered the strength to step out of the dark cloud. I calmly suggested, for the first time, that he take a dose of morphine.

He took my advice.

I encouraged him to lie back, to become quieter, softer, to let the morphine work, to let his brain endorphins work with the morphine.

19

"I don't think I can, but I'll try," he said as he lay down on his side.

I rubbed his back. "Relax your feet," I said, "feet relaxing … calves growing soft, knees relax ... thigh muscles becoming like jelly ... and up the body to the torso. Relax the chest, let the breaths come easier, breathing in and out easier now.... Be gentle with yourself ... peace coming."

By then he breathed much more slowly. "Gently, now ... ease your shoulders," I said, as I rubbed ... "and your neck. Your face, too, becomes less drawn, more relaxed ... and your scalp ... and your mind. Gentle with yourself now, letting go of the fears. They have served you well sometimes, but you can let go of them now. Just relax your mind. You can breathe easily now, slowly in and out, easy now."... And he was asleep.

Noon the next day. He was still asleep. He wasn't struggling at all. His breaths flowed in an easy rhythm.

A month passed. It was Friday, October 2.

I'd been gone for awhile and John was sitting on a chair in JW's room where JW was sitting up with his shirt off, hot and sweaty. His abdominal and chest muscles were pumping away as though he were at the end of a marathon. I sat down by him and put my hand on his hip. He lay down. My own voice was playing on the tape recorder in his room. It was the meditation about the special place with the silver star. JW closed his eyes. I sat on his bed, touching him, caressing him. He looked at me after I had been with him for a few minutes. "Hi," he said. His voice was weak, but affectionate.

"Hi."

He closed his eyes again, seemed more relaxed, and in a few minutes fell asleep. His respirations decreased from near forty to just over twenty a minute.

John and I went into the dining room to eat.

A short time later, JW called out for help.

John and I hurried to his room. He was sitting up on the bed. His chest rose and fell markedly with each breath. The area below his Adam's apple formed a deep crater. His lips were more ashen than usual. I sat down and put my hand on him again. "Why are you sitting up?"

"The breathing—it's so hard. Can I have a little morphine?"

He hadn't had any since morning. I gave him ten milligrams. He lay down again, but continued to struggle. I suggested he close his eyes, flow with the music or the words on the tape. Minutes later, I said strongly, "Find that wisdom within you, JW, the wisdom that knows what to do. You're fighting so hard. Find a way to stop the fighting."

After that, he repeated, "Calm, calm, calm, relax, relax," over and over. Out loud, strongly. Shortly after seven o'clock, I asked him if he had taken any Proventil, another medication to help make breathing a little easier. He shook his head, no.

"Would you like one?" I asked.

He nodded. John, sitting on the other side of the bed, handed him a pill.

JW took the pill in his hand, began to sit up, then crumpled, falling back on the bed limp.

My arms flew around him. I could feel some breathing. I wasn't sure what his heart was doing, but I knew he was dying. "Love is around you JW, a rosy cloud of love, so pink and beautiful. Love is all around you. I love you, JW. You are love itself."

His breathing slowed. Breaths came many seconds apart as the minutes elapsed. The breaths were shallow, not labored. "Grandpa and Watson are with you, loving you. You can find Grandpa and Watson now, if you want, maybe George Washington, too. You're not alone, JW. I'm with you. I'll always be with you. Dad will always be with you. You will always be with us."

His breathing slowed.

With dripping eyes, I looked at JW who seemed unconscious, "It's okay to let go."

He nodded, just a slight movement, and I thought I detected a hint of a smile.

His breaths became slower, with many seconds elapsing between them. Shallow, gentle breaths, more gentle than he had breathed in months.

John was there next to JW, caressing him. "I love you, JW."

There was never a moment of death, but rather a slipping away. The process had continued for fifteen minutes or so. At some point John and I knew that his physical body no longer lived.

We continued to touch JW and hold him. I stroked his back and his hair, saying, "I love you," over and over. "We are two hearts combined, you and me."

And the minutes passed. There was a gentle transition from drop to ocean.

I telephoned the doctor on call, Dr. Kile. "JW died a few minutes ago."

"I'll be over in a few minutes."

"Don't rush. We're okay here."

"Well, if it's okay, I'll finish what I'm doing and be over in a half hour or so."

At the time of death, strangely enough, I felt spacious and whole, with feelings related to those in the moments following my son Greg's birth. Peaceful, complete. Interwoven, as if a self did not exist. Birth and death occupied a similar space, with life flowing in and out.

In an other-worldly place, I saw a luminous cloud raining tiny bright threads into Greg as his eyes opened wide in wonder, legs kicking, arms flailing, and body glowing. That cloud opened again, with the luminescent flecks floating up from JW to become part of it. JW's eyes were closed, his body radiant and still. So still.

In those moments, the fog that shielded me from knowing mystery warmed and dissolved.

John and I moved mechanically without planning and with no urgency. I called Marayel and Orien from the cordless phone by the bed. We sat with JW, caressing, talking, and hugging.

John called Lynner Funeral Home. Jack Lynner, the mortician, would come. "Wait until nine o'clock or after," John said. "We need some time." He looked down at JW and his tears fell directly on JW's face. I wept gently while I ran my fingers through JW's hair, all the while telling him he was not alone and encouraging him to seek my spirit as well as that of Watson and Grandpa.

Dr. Kile came. Yes, JW was officially dead. She only stayed a few minutes.

Marayel and Orien came. Everyone gathered in JW's room, three or four of us on the bed at a time. All of us talked to JW from time to time. I called my folks and Greg. John called his mom and Misty.

I lay down next to him. "I've spent so much time on this bed with you, JW. I remember you telling me how good it felt to have me here." I caressed his face. "I love you, I love you."

Lady, a basset hound JW had chosen the previous spring, put her paws up on the side of the bed and looked at JW.

Jack Lynner came. We talked about the arrangements. We would not have JW embalmed. There would be a ceremony on Sunday, which Orien would lead. There would be no announcement about the funeral on the radio. We would call those people who needed to know.

"Oh, JW, how much fun it was to get Lady! And when you ate all the s'mores at Castle Haven. And the night we all ate Popsicles sitting here on the bed."

We all cried from time to time, not heaves, not sobs, but a gentle dripping from the sea within.

It was time for the undertaker to take JW's body away. John couldn't watch. He went into the library and Marayel followed him, to be with him. I gave Jack Lynner a meditation tape with my voice and asked him to keep playing it for JW at the funeral home. I tucked Oscar, a stuffed white harp seal, underneath his cheek.

"JW, you won't be alone."

I picked up our other basset hound, BJ, who gave JW a last sloppy lick. Jack began to cover JW with a white sheet, asking if it was all right to do so. I nodded and thought of my vision just after his transplant. Jack and Orien put him on the litter. Then Jack zipped the body bag around him, and they picked up the litter.

It was time for JW to exit the house for the last time. I held the front door open for Orien and Jack. "I'll miss you, JW," I said as they started down the stairs, heading for the white hearse.

Marayel and Orien left after asking if John and I wanted them to stay. I shook my head. "I want to spend some time alone with John."

John and I hugged, and cried, and talked. I straightened up JW's room. I made the fold-out bed into a couch.

John picked up a bottle of medications. "We need to get rid of these pills."

I took the medicine bottles and flushed the pills down the toilet, one after the other, methodically closing my chapter of high tech medicine.

John turned off the oxygen concentrator. It was quiet then, without the sound of the rushing air. It was still and tranquil.

We turned on the front porch light. We took the dogs for a walk down by the river, the first time we had gone for a walk together for a long time.

After midnight John and I went to bed. Neither of us slept. We got up around 2:30 and talked and cried some more. We had a glass of wine, then went to bed again, but sleep never came for me. Around six o'clock we got up.

I put on the coffee.

John put on a record of Strauss' *Blue Danube*.

I straightened up the house.

The following evening, the family gathered at the funeral home—my mom and Pops; Aunt Elynor; my sister, Sue; her husband, Larry; and their two kids, Ruth and Jon; my brother, Doug; his wife, Marie; and their son, Brook.

Misty placed a yellow rose in the casket with JW, a rose from the arrangement sent by Marayel. I put two pictures underneath JW's hands, one of the whole family, and one of our dogs, Bella, Barney, BJ, and Lady. I lit the candle we'd brought from home, one of the succession of candles we'd kept burning during the last month.

I had not thought of JW as angelic, but the word *angelic* came to mind as I looked at him. My mom began to sob. I did, too, as I hugged Mom, who was thinking about my brother, Bobby. Again a child had died; then a son, now a grandson.

Sunday came. I spent the morning making funeral folders on the computer, a task Jack Lynner was afraid I wouldn't get done. He'd encouraged me to let the funeral home make them, as they usually did, and suggested that it might be too stressful for me.

I needed to do it. A stranger's words wouldn't do.

Led by friend Orien Vick, all of us gather to share in our love and to honor JW, to weep at the loss we feel as his body returns to dust, to cry and to laugh at the precious memories he has given for us to weave into ourselves, to revere the gifts of learning and inspiration he gave us, to sense joy in the freedom he finds as he sheds his shell, and to feel his continuing presence among and within each of us, knowing we are one.

We also honor the life of the woman who began sharing her heart and her lungs with JW on December 20, 1990.

JW's body is just a little part of the light that shines within his heart. Even when he is asleep, he is awake in every shining star. He is me and I am him. You are me and I am you.

I had modified the last sentence from the book, *All I See Is Part of Me*, by Chara Curtis and Cynthia Aldrich.

At the funeral home, the family gathered and kissed and touched JW for the last time. Orien was there, having arrived earlier to set up the music system he brought from home. Yanni's *Keys to Imagination* was playing.

John and I kissed JW farewell. I put my hand on his and said, "You are not alone. We have to close the casket now. We won't see your body again. I am with you wherever you are."

John said, "I love you, JW." A drop fell on JW's cheek. "I know I'll see my dad again, and I know I'll see you again."

We closed the casket together.

It was time for the ceremony. The chairs were arranged in a circle, which needed to be expanded since more people than expected arrived. JW in his closed casket was one of sixty or seventy people who formed the circle. Many of his classmates were there. It felt surprisingly good to see his classmates and friends.

Orien began, in his deep melodious voice, by talking about names. "JW, for instance," he said, "is simply that which he is called, not who he is. He is much more. When we label a person with a name or a description—black, white, pretty, psychotic—we limit our vision of that individual. When we name a bird or a flower, we think we know what kind of a thing it is. But an eagle is much more than *eagle*. JW is much more than the still body now lying in that coffin."

Orien invited those gathered to tell JW stories, and he told one himself. "JW told me once that he was so afraid to ride the Corkscrew at Valleyfair, but he rode it once, then again, and ended up riding it most of the day, still a bit afraid. He was afraid of death, too, but he faced it, encountered it, and went into it."

Mr. McCoss, the school principal, told about JW coming to him, at age ten, having just moved to Granite Falls from Shakopee. "You don't know who I am," Johnny, as he was called then, had said, "but you will. I want to borrow twenty dollars to go back to Shakopee on the bus."

Marie, a girl friend from school said, "I met JW in tenth grade. He gave me a lot. He told me never to give up in life, even if I wanted to. He showed me that life has more meaning than I thought it did. Because of him, I'll never give up in life."

Linda Linssen, one of his teachers, said, "JW was one of the good people in this world. I admired his courage and positive attitude, even when I knew he felt miserable. I enjoyed reading his sensitive, honest writing. This fall I assigned a seat in my classroom to JW, and even though he didn't return, the desk never seemed empty."

Others told stories.

Orien read *All I see is Part of Me*, a children's book full of magnificent pictures and deep wisdom. It was the book that Orien and Marayel had brought to JW a couple of weeks earlier. On that day, Orien sat on JW's bed as he read the book out loud and JW's eyes had the look of a four-year-old watching a puppy.

The ceremony ended. Twenty cars formed a procession to the cemetery thirty miles away. We hadn't designated pallbearers. Lynner simply announced at the end of the ceremony, "Whoever would like to carry the casket at the cemetery, please gather by the hearse when we get there."

At the cemetery, John and I slowly walked down the hill to the grave-site. I looked up the hill. The casket was coming, carried by my friends, Jude Arnold and Nancy Hone, by Pops, my son Greg, my brother Doug, and brother-in-law Larry. Nancy's little poodle, Biscuit, was bounding down the hill with JW and the casket bearers. *JW would like this,* I reflected. *He'd like having a puppy here.*

They positioned the casket above the ground. Everyone held hands around the grave. My mom stood on her son's grave, Bobby's grave, directly across from me. My eyes met hers.

"As I bury my son," I said, in a moment that seemed timeless, "I see my mom standing on the grave of her son, my brother, the son that she buried forty-seven years ago. I am with her now. A mother, a daughter, both burying their sons. It comforts me knowing that JW will lie by Bobby and by Daddy."

Nancy Hone said, "A couple of weeks ago, while massaging JW, I saw a mahogany chariot coming for him, a chariot led by loving spirits. Perhaps two of those spirits that came to carry JW home are your brother and your dad."

"Let's spend a few moments focusing love on JW," I said. I closed my eyes and, as I had held JW in love at Healing Circle, I did again. Once more the shade disappeared. Things were clear, yet formless. My skin no longer formed a boundary. This was a sacred time.

"JW's body will now be held by Mother Earth, blanketed by her rich soil. That which was dust again becomes dust," Orien said.

It appeared that no one was going to lower the body. I guessed it was customary for the family to leave with the casket still suspended above the grave, that most people couldn't stand the sight of the body being lowered.

John approached the grave-digger. "We want the body put into the ground."

JW's body was let down into the grave. Marayel dropped the rest of the yellow roses on top of the casket. John and I took a long final look, then slowly turned and ascended the hill.

At the top of the hill, John turned his head back toward the grave. "Marcia, turn around. Look at the hillside, at the beauty. We need to remember this beauty."

Brilliant reds, subtle oranges and golds, bright yellows, and shades of green were illuminated by the warm sun in the western sky. Oak trees, maples, pines, and ashes.

On Monday evening, John and I, along with John's mother Alice, gathered around the candle that had been burning the seventy-two hours since JW's death, the candle that had adorned the top of his casket during the ceremony at the funeral home.

"JW," I said, "you may wish to go a little more distant from us now. If you want to go, it's okay to leave, to go wherever there is most love and joy for you. You are always with me and me with you."

"We'll light your candle on special occasions, JW," John said. Then he gently blew out the candle. Alice began sobbing. I held her closely while her tears wet my face.

For many days I felt a deep hole in my chest—aching, longing, and empty. Tears came often, especially while I drove alone in the car. I talked with JW, and cried as I drove.

"JW, you are free now, free from your body that anchored you. Now you can soar toward the stars, dive with the seagulls, fly like Jonathan." ... " Thank you for coming into my life, JW, for helping me learn that I am you and you are me." ... "I miss you, JW. I love you. I wish I had told you that more often."

Although an autonomic response in me paid attention to driving, I was in a semi-hypnotic state. Telling JW I loved him, I realized I was talking to myself. *Loving you, I love me. Loving me, I love you. Accepting you, I accept me.*

And one day about a month after he died, while I was driving home from work, a ball of warmth entered my chest. How warm it felt, as if a light bulb had turned on in my heart. I felt the hole in my chest closing over. JW entered me there, had come to stay in one of the zillions of concurrent beingnesses that he is.

He was not lost, as some of the sympathy cards had suggested. His energy was somewhere. At least in some holographic sense, I knew he was part of me, more a part of me than he was before his physical death.

As the months passed, I sometimes criticized myself for not feeling more grief. *I wonder how I can talk about his death now, think about him, without tearing, without suffering,* I'd say to myself. I felt serene or pensive when I thought of him, not anguished. I would know it if he were suffering, and would feel it myself.

Suffering, I thought, came from the illusion of boxes that separate one being from another, the cubicles described by words, descriptions of experience.

Many people tried to comfort me by describing JW's death as a tragedy. To me, to call his death a tragedy was to characterize his life in terms of its finality, as just another untimely loss.

I looked at the clouds. I looked at the land, and I knew JW was in the clouds and on the land, unfettered by the physical body. No separation, no suffering.

Through JW I learned to accept mystery. I needed no intellectual explanation.

Mystery, sacred mystery.

The best hope for preservation of human life on earth is for human beings to come to the type of spiritual connection that happens at death, to become a part of all existence, rather than separate, discrete elements.

That idea was the edge along which I walked. I hoped I would approach my own death, when it came, with a similar sense of adventure as when John and I had set out for Alaska on our motorcycles. With curiosity and wonder.

I thought about what I would have done differently if I could go back several months. *I would have hugged a little more. As JW held his head in his hands, I would have honored that time for him, with less distress, less demand to help. And, I did what I did. I honor what I did as well as what he did. I honor his gentleness and his ability to let my love in and his out. So many times I think of that moment about an hour or two before he began to walk the spirit path. As I sat on his bed, my hand on his hip, he looked up and said, "Hi."*

I long for that moment again, and then I realize that I'll always have that moment, and need not yearn for it.

I was discovering the human being that lived in my body. I found myself coming closer to the edge of the known. I retreated, then took a step closer. Exploration into the unknown beckoned. *Perhaps all that I question about life and death is as simple and complex as living my life as an exploration and accepting death as a return to unity.*

Approaching death with honor, rather than fear, would let me approach life with awe. Rather than viewing landscapes through the spattered windshield of a car and fearing the slippery roads ahead, I would ride through life on a motorcycle, with the wind blowing through my hair as I approached steep cliffs and endless oceans.

John and I would move to Animal Farm. I'd cook with wood and discover how to live with fewer modern conveniences. I'd have gardens, would learn about medicinal herbs and grow them. We'd erect a teepee—a special place to talk and to sit in silence. I'd watch the summer sun rise in the northeastern sky and the winter sun set in the southwest. John would build an observatory to peer into the galaxies. I would look out on a prairie blizzard and curl up by the dogs in front of a blazing fire.

Eight months after JW died, John and I moved to our land. We'd finished the skeleton of the house, but had no inside walls or running water or electricity, at first.

Two months later, I sold my Olds Cutlass Ciera and started using JW's royal blue Geo Metro, which John and I named *The JW.* I often talked to him when I drove.

A delicate yellow rose. I'm so glad I brought you that yellow rose. Although the exquisite blossoms are material, and you no longer are, I want to give you yellow roses. I don't know where to find the Self you found at death, JW. But, every so often, if you look, you'll find your grave adorned with a single yellow rose.

I felt the soft touch of JW's delicate hands on mine as I turned onto County Road 22, heading toward home.

Celandine

Chelidonium majus
Perennial

For "gallbladder headaches," similar to migraines, when bile is congested and plugging the bile duct, celandine should be taken in tiny doses (one drop of the tincture). Celandine helps break down fibrous growths and is useful for warts, fibroid tumors, and even malignant abdominal tumors and skin cancer. It is especially helpful for people who have a yellowish complexion due to liver dysfunction. It helps detoxify the liver, improving metabolism.

A bushy perennial growing eighteen to twenty-four inches high, this plant self seeds, so is mildly invasive. It likes sun and good drainage.

Tincture the aerial parts and use in small or homeopathic doses. Use the fresh juice from the stems on warts or skin cancers. The leaves, stems, and flowers can be juiced in a juice extractor and saved in the refrigerator for up to six months for external application.

Chamomile

Matricaria chamomilla
Self seeding annual (German); Perennial (Roman)

Chamomile is a well known mildly sedative herb that is antispasmotic, soothing, a tonic for the nervous system, and useful for many digestive upsets as well as being an aid to sleep. Chamomile baths are helpful for the entire nervous system. Chamomile steam used either by breathing directly over an almost boiling infusion or from a vaporizer eases symptoms of colds and sinusitis. Chamomile was a traditional herb for fussy and/or teething babies. Wood says it is especially suitable for persons who are petulant, quarrelsome, inclined to be angry, or out-of-sorts and impatient, particularly when sick or during menses. Chamomile is diaphoretic and helps with mild, recurrent fevers by bringing on a sweat and bringing forth the illness so the body can combat it more effectively. Applied topically, chamomile soothes and heals burns and skin wounds.

Chamomile, whether German, an annual, or Roman, a spreading mat-forming perennial used in lawns, is raised easily from seed and self seeds readily, so is mildly invasive and rarely needs reseeding if grown in the same spot. It produces small (less than one inch) daisy-like flowers. German chamomile grows more upright than Roman, reaching a height of about one foot, and has a higher proportion of volatile oil than Roman, so is the primary variety used in herbal preparations. It grows best in well drained, neutral soil in the sun.

In addition to many other virtues, Gerard said of chamomile, "The decoction made in wine and drunke expelleth the dead child and afterbirth speedily and cleanfeth thofe parts."

The flowers are harvested when fully open and used fresh in tinctures or infusions or dried for later use. Freezing the flowers retains their volatile oil better than drying them. In addition, fresh chamomile flowers can be infused in olive or other oil and then made into ointments.

Chickweed

Stellaria media
Spreading perennial

Chickweed is an herb to consider for any internal inflammation. It decongests the lymphatic system and is a diuretic that regulates fluid in the body, removing fluid if needed, holding on to it if the body needs the fluid. It is used for fatty tumors, bronchitis, and ear infections. Externally, use chickweed as an oil or ointment for eczema and vaginitis, as well as for pruritis and even skin cancers. Chickweed is a nutritional powerhouse and is a healthy addition to any green salad. It contains vitamin C, B6, B12, D, rutin, and beta carotene, magnesium, iron, calcium, potassium, zinc, phosphorus, manganese, sodium, copper, and silicon. It also helps increase the absorption of many nutrients.

Chickweed ointment

Pick fresh chickweed and fill a glass jar, packing lightly. Cover with olive oil. Let sit in a sunny place for 7-10 days. Strain. Discard the herb into your compost. Add 2-3 drops tincture of benzoin (as a preservative). Store the oil at this point or use to make an ointment, as follows:

10 ounces infused chickweed oil
1/2 ounce beeswax.

Heat together until wax is melted. Immediately pour into small containers. Cover.

Chickweed is a short grass-like spreading "weed" with tiny white flowers. It tolerates sun and shade, is found on the edge of many gardens and other lawn areas, and is a nuisance to gardeners, but a joy to herbalists.

Harvest the aerial parts just before or during bloom. Use as a tisane or tincture or make an infused oil, then add beeswax to make an ointment.

Chives

Allium schoenoprasum
Perennial

Chives is rarely thought of for its therapeutic value, although the leaves are high in vitamin C, folic acid, and potassium as well as calcium and iron. Due to its sulphur compounds, the plant has medicinal qualities similar to garlic and onion, although to a lesser degree. Chives also stimulates the appetite and promotes good digestion, contributing to its culinary value. With its mild onion-like flavor, chives is used primarily in cooking and in salads and is especially good with potatoes and eggs, such as in a potato salad or omelet.

Chives is a clump forming perennial with slender bulbs. It grows up to fifteen inches high with cylindrical hollow leaves and purple flowers. It spreads over time. The leaves re-grow after being cut. The flowers are showy and they, too, can be eaten, making an attractive addition to salads.

Use the leaves fresh in cooking or dry for later use.

Cilantro/coriander

Coriandrum sativum
Self-seeding annual

Cilantro is not particularly noted for its healing value, but aromatherapists use it as an anti-rheumatic. Coriander seeds freshen the breath after eating garlic. Tea made from the seeds helps relieve indigestion. Coriander is used in the cooking cuisines of Mexico, South American, and Asia.

This is two herbs in one. Cilantro is the herb in its young leafy form before it bolts and flowers. It is one of the oldest known herbs, having been found in ancient Egyptian tombs. Often an ingredient of salsa, cilantro blends well with other spicy ingredients and the roots as well as the leaves can be used. Coriander is the plant in its seed form. The taste is very different than cilantro, having a sweet spicy quality. It is used in curries, is a main ingredient of Garam Masala, a favorite Indian cooking spice blend, and is also used in cakes and breads and in flavoring liqueurs such as gin and vermouth. Its taste goes well with apples. Apple ginger-coriander pie is a wonderful dessert.

This annual herb should be sown at intervals because it bolts quickly, so is in its cilantro form for only a week or two. It self seeds well, so you will find it growing where you planted it in a previous year. Harvest the leaves before they start becoming smaller as they prepare to bolt. Cilantro is best used fresh and loses flavor upon drying. Coriander seeds are harvested late in the season before frosts, but when the seed is dry. To clean them from the chaff, put the seeds in a large strainer and bounce them outside on a windy day.

Use the fresh leaves and the seeds primarily in cooking.

Curried chicken with coriander

For the chicken and stock:
1 onion
1 carrot
1 stalk celery
3 1/2 lb. roasting chicken (or, if necessary to substitute, use 2 lbs. chicken breast)
1 bay leaf
3 sprigs parsley
3 sprigs lovage (optional)
1 tsp. sea salt and 6 peppercorns

For the curry sauce:
3 T shredded coconut
1 large onion
2 medium cloves garlic—or one large
1/4 cup butter
1 T curry powder
1 tsp. ground turmeric
1/4 tsp. ground cumin seed
1 T ground coriander
1/8 tsp. ground hot pepper—or more if you like it hot
1 T red currant or grape jelly
Juice of 1 lime
1 T flour
1/4 cup plain yogurt

Peel and halve the onion. Chop the celery and carrot coarsely. Put the vegetables in a saucepan with the chicken. Poach for 2-2 1/2 hours. Lift out the chicken when tender. When the chicken is cool enough to handle, remove the skin and bones and cut meat into small pieces. Set aside.

Strain the liquid and discard the vegetables to your compost heap.

To make the curry sauce, pour half the stock over the coconut in a bowl. Let sit for 15 minutes. Peel onion and chop finely. Peel garlic cloves and crush. Melt butter in large saucepan and cook onion gently until pale golden, adding the garlic halfway through. Sprinkle on the curry powder and herbs, stirring all of the time. Pour in the remaining stock. Simmer gently 15 minutes. Add jelly and lime. Pour coconut mixture through strainer into curry sauce, pushing lightly with a spoon to extract all of the liquid. Stir the flour into the yogurt and add to the curry sauce, continuing to stir. Add chicken pieces. Reheat, stirring. Add chopped almonds and coriander or basil. Let sit covered for 5 minutes. Serve on boiled rice or couscous.

Home on the Prairie

When I first saw the land that was to become our home the grasses were tall and hundreds, maybe thousands, of Monarch butterflies danced among the leaves in the trees, their orange and black wings producing a quivering that made the air seem alive.

"Was I right?" asked John. "Does this piece of prairie tug at your soul, call you to make it our home?

I looked around. A grove of trees defined the north edge of the property, lining the enchanted entrance to the land. Like waves of grain, the uncut summer prairie grasses flowed in the gentle breeze as if lullabying a child to sleep. Another grove of ashes and box elders, along with one magnificent towering cottonwood, stood in the southeast corner of the five acres.

"I think it's perfect," I replied dreamily.

We'd been searching for cleared land on which to build a home with our own four hands, a place where our puppies could run freely, where I could garden and John could fly gliders and craft things of wood. We wanted a place where the physical work of tending the gardens and chopping wood for heat and cooking could replace the frenetic city life driven by money and accumulation of objects.

The grasses were nearly waist deep in this island surrounded by corn fields to the north, south, and east and a cattle pasture to the west. It was as if the prairie had made a nest here, a home for wild life, whether deer, coyotes, owls, or humans. The whole five acres rose in elevation from the surrounding fields and meandered in rolling terrain, unlike the flat prairie all around.

John and I walked hand in hand and I pointed out clumps of chicory, of vervain, of yellow sweet clover. We lay in the grasses and made angels, as if we were school children making them in the snow.

Yes, we decided that day, we'd like to make this place our home. We'd call it Animal Farm. It would be a place where rabbits could play a game of tag with our basset hounds, but never be caught, a place where we'd welcome toads, garter snakes, and earthworms to help sustain the fertile soil.

We'd been losing our souls to our workaholic lives as city dwellers. We still had enough spirit, though, to recognize the value of simple living, to appreciate the chirping of crickets, the grand whistle of tundra swans on their migration, and the fragrant scent of wild roses. We'd longed for a more natural life that would mean harder physical work, fewer modern contrivances, and freedom from the invented deadlines and social pretenses of business and city life. We'd read stories that told of trials and successes experienced by others who had used nails and boards to turn their dreams into homes and it fortified our courage to do the same.

A decade later I drive into the driveway, still lined with the grove of trees we call the north woods. I remember the first day and see the butterflies dancing and the grasses waving. I look again and see a cedar-sided storage shed and a forest green workshop that includes a small shop called Honey & Herbs.

There stands the house, a gable and lean-to structure sided with cedar and redwood. I see the power poles, upon which we hung the house as its foundation, and envision the day when we planted those twelve poles into the six-foot holes we'd dug by hand. The thirty-footers took pounds of sweat, along with grunting and swearing and praying, to maneuver them into place. Oddly enough, when I stood back to admire our work on that day over ten years ago, the huge poles looked like toothpicks sticking out of the dirt as if seen by Alice in Wonderland.

The greeting of our three basset hounds interrupts my reflections. The dogs now have just five acres to roam, not the miles they had until Papa Tracker wandered too far, was unable to find his way home, and was found near starvation a month later. A lattice fence now forms an attractive border to the north of the house, with woven wire fencing completing the playground for the dogs. It limits their freedom, but provides the dogs with a measure of safety and rids me of anxiety about their whereabouts.

After greeting the dogs with a pat on each head, I return to my survey of our prairie home. The herb gardens to the west show that fall has claimed the chlorophyll of the milkvetch and milk thistle, the green of summer having given way to yellow and brown. The chicory still blooms blue unaware of the coming harvest of its roots. The St. John's wort has lost its yellow flowers, but its green leaves prevail, and the feverfew is in full bloom, its daisy-like flowers and bright green leaves appearing oblivious to the coming frost.

I walk around the house where I've already tilled the vegetable gardens under, except for the late producing tomatoes and peppers. Mocking the intensity of their heat, the tiny red Thai peppers look delectable against their shiny green leaves. Many of the bell peppers are now sweetly red in their ripeness.

The groves still grow wild, with downed branches and high grasses and weeds left to provide habitat for the woodchucks, squirrels, and rabbits. We mow three acres of grass, lush now with the wet fall. The green grass provides contrast to the yellow, red, and rust leaves that have fallen from the maples and oaks we've planted and from the black willow, elder, and ashes that lived here before we did.

The land reflects the balance we've achieved in our lives, the wild and the cultivated living in respectful harmony, a harmony broken occasionally with the poisoning of a pocket gopher and the swatting of mosquitoes and flies. The compromise of a fence for the dogs is a metaphor for the concessions we've made in our living. In the winter the wood cook stove provides heat while radiating the smell of baking bread. The microwave and gas grill are useful summer tools. We're connected to the internet, but have forsaken the intrusion of television.

Our place on the prairie in not an idyllic paradise graced only with wonder and happiness, but sitting on my deck as a warm autumn day turns to evening, my soul sparkles in the waning sunlight while the dogs frolic in the grassy shadows.

White

Even the power lines are beautiful. Sparkling white lines the needles of the pines, outlines the tall grasses, and defines the dormant stalks of the mint and sage left standing in the garden. The small branches and twigs of the deciduous trees look like huge soft feathers, covered as they are with a thick layer of white crystals.

An abandoned barn, turned grey now with boards rotten and crumbling, displays itself today. Its tilt to the east caused by the deteriorating foundation is defined by the stark whiteness of the grove of trees to the northwest and the bushes on the east gone wild now. Outlined by the hoar frost backdrop, the barn looks enchanted as if revealing that it has many untold stories.

As I travel along the highway, a red barn is brilliant against the background of white. Snow covers the ground. The roof shingles, usually grey, are now crystalline white. Frosted branches outline themselves against the blue-grey sky. Farms hardly noticeable in the usual rush of getting somewhere are colorful, set off as they are by the crystals covering the shrubs and criss-crossing the charcoal trunks and main branches of the ash trees and taller cottonwoods. The field-wire fences, usually invisible, define property edges and cattle pastures.

Bright sunlight adds radiance to the crystalline painting. White crystals, floating in the air as they begin to shed themselves from the trees, look like gently falling snow.

Surely the palm lined boulevards of the warm south don't compare in beauty to a sunlit hoar frost morning in the frigid northland.

Four Blue Eggs

When I lived in the city I could believe the myth that my species is separate from the others, not simply by degrees but by a critical gap. Living in the country, my surroundings inform me that I am part of nature, as much a part as are the birds, the cat, and the plants in this story.

The nest, built on the fence by the shed, held four blue eggs, robin eggs. Perfection, I thought, as I gazed at the eggs. Delicate. Vibrant blue, a shade somewhere between the color of the western sky on a cloudless summer morning and the turquoise of clear ocean waters. Gazing at the eggs, I bathed in the innocence of childhood. I was transported back in time to age three or four when I first saw robin eggs, first knew that eggs crack and baby birds emerge, catapulted back to that time when I first saw fledglings attempting their maiden flights and watched as their awkwardness turned to grace.

Mama Robin came back and sat on those eggs. She sat and she sat.

John and I were building a workshop. The north end of the shop was within twenty feet of the nest, so I was there to see Mama Robin sit. Hours, days, of sitting. I marveled at Mama's patience, at her ability to sit so long and so still.

When I ventured too close, I saw her beak open. Sounds almost too soft to hear in the roaring wind told me to go away. I pitied Mama Robin sitting on her nest as days stretched into weeks. Not only did she have to put up with the shrill scream of power saws and drills, the hammering of nails being driven, but she had to listen to hour after hour of the country western music John liked. I would have gone mad sitting there. She, who was accustomed to the trilling of blackbirds, the croaking of frogs, the rustling of wind, and perhaps an occasional meow of a cat, had to listen to the blaring of synthesized music and screaming guitars. Mozart, Prokofief, Strauss, or even country ballads, might have been okay, but not raucous country wailing and screeching. But, music or no music, she sat and she sat.

One morning when I looked into the nest I only two eggs. Two inch-long blobs of ectoplasm with tiny tufts of hair replaced the other eggs. Later that day there was just one beautiful egg in the nest. By the next day, there were four blobs of pulsing life, not as beautiful as those blue eggs, but they, even more than the eggs, tapped the pool of childlike wonder hidden within me.

Mama sat to warm the tiny birds. She'd leave the nest briefly and return with food for them. Within a couple of days I saw tiny yellow beaks poking out of the nest stretching toward Mama's beak. I hadn't noticed Daddy Robin before, but now I saw he helped to feed the young.

Mama began to leave the nest more often, searching for food, I imagined, or perhaps enjoying flight and other adventures. The babies were growing large enough to keep each other warm. Feathers emerged. I saw eyes, still closed, as the baby robins grew. Their coloring changed daily, their size by the hour.

I felt sorry for the little creatures whose music their first days was guitars and crowing human voices instead of leaves growing, grasses rustling, insects flying. I turned off the radio whenever John wasn't around.

Mama still opened her beak and told me to go away when I came too close.

We normally used the fenced stockade that had become Robin's home as a place to contain our basset hounds—Barney and Lady—when we left Animal Farm. A doggy door between the stockade and the shed allowed the dogs shelter when they wished, grass and sun when they wanted. Ever since we'd seen the four blue eggs, however, we'd kept the dogs out, fearful that they'd frighten Mama away.

Meanwhile, there was Caesar to contend with. He was a feral cat who'd come to our place the previous fall. Sometime in October we first saw this black and white cat eating food from a dish we left in the shed for the dogs. Later we saw him crossing the yard or returning to the dog food dish, but he'd scurry away if he saw one of us. John started putting out milk. We'd find the dish empty, but never actually saw the cat drinking.

I threw some leftover pie crust dough into the compost bucket outside the door while preparing Thanksgiving dinner. I heard the bucket tip over and, opening the door, saw the cat running away. I bought some dry cat food and placed a dish on the straw bale by the door.

Cat ate it.

Winter came. The cat made his home under our house, which is built on poles. Straw bales stacked around the house provided some insulation. It provided a warmer place for the cat, as well, who could find spaces in the straw to climb in and out from under the house.

I put out chicken fat and leftover ham and turkey. The cat would dart away when I opened the door and watch me put food in his dish from ten yards away. He would come to eat when I closed the door. With his sleek coat, he looked healthy and strong.

Twice during that winter the temperature reached thirty-two degrees below zero. The cat came for food two or three times a day. When hungry, he stood outside the window and meowed. We kept feeding him and he survived the coldest Minnesota winter in fifty years.

By May, the cat was getting expensive and we'd named him Caesar. He'd become finicky when food was plentiful. He had us well trained and would eat only canned cat food, not dry. He still liked leftover chicken or ham, but not hamburger. He didn't let me touch him, but would shyly sit a foot or two from his dish while I filled it. Caesar would eat four cans of cat food a day if I provided it. I worried that he might have forgotten how to catch mice, although I did see him watching a striped gopher intently and occasionally saw him eyeing some goldfinches that came to the feeder.

I knew those baby robins were out in that nest, vulnerable there on the fence post. I fed Caesar well, hoping he'd leave the birds alone.

"The baby robins are gone," John yelled to me one morning a couple of weeks after they hatched.

"Oh no," I shrieked, knowing they were too young to fly.

I found some shredded body parts covered with downy feathers on the ground next to the fence. I sat down on the ground by the feathers and cupped my chin in my hands, "Oh, Mama Robin, you tried so hard to create new life," I said to Mama wherever she was. "You sat and you sat. You brought food so diligently."

"Oh Mama Robin," I cried, "You gave your babies a bit of life. You gave me the chance to see your patience, to see your babies growing. Thank you for that. I hurt with you, for I am sure you hurt, sure that you screeched in horror as you saw your first baby torn asunder, then your second, third, and finally, watching helplessly, saw your last baby killed.

"I think Caesar ate your babies. I played a part in this story. I helped keep Caesar alive. I tried to protect you and your babies, and now they are dead."

When I saw Caesar, I angrily scolded him for killing the baby robins and for wasting some of his kill. I ignored him sitting by his dish looking for a hand-out.

Tears wet my cheeks. My intellect accepted that this was nature's way, but I needed time to be sad for the deaths, sad for Mama Robin, sad for me. We mamas have a hard time seeing our babies die. JW died when he was just seventeen. I couldn't protect him from death anymore than I could protect the baby robins.

I closed my eyes and the images came. Perfect little blue eggs. Beautiful black and white cat. Screaming power saws, blaring radio. Perfect tiny yellow beaks. Tiny bird legs strewn on the ground.

I went to the garden and pulled weeds. I took care to preserve the tiny blades of onion and the wee carrot stalks growing among the weeds. When I pulled a little carrot from its home in the earth, I replanted it, hoping it would grow. There were too many carrots, too many onions, too many cabbages. I should have thinned them, but I had trouble thinning plants in the garden, couldn't decide which should live, which should not, so I let nature decide.

Barney Basset came to visit me in the garden, stepped on a six inch tomato plant, and broke its stem. "Oh, little tomato, oh little birdies," I wailed. I even felt some sadness for the weeds I pulled. Yes, I know weeds are weeds because they are so prolific, I told myself.

But weeds are life. I killed to eat, just as Caesar did. Like him, I didn't take care to save any edible or medicinal weeds, just discarded them there on the ground not far from baby robin remains.

As evening approached my anger at Caesar dissipated. I knew that Caesar carried out his nature just as Mama Robin did. I sat on the deck as the sun descended and wondered about my own character. I considered my own killing of creatures—the frogs that hop in front of my car wheels during a rain, the birds that fly into my windows, the snakes I cut apart with the whirling of the blade on my lawnmower. I recognized my own complicity in the violence of nature, including my eating of meat that others kill.

With the dogs by my side, I watched as the western sky displayed swathes of orange and pinks and saw beauty and goodness in nature as well as the pain.

Colors of spring

The virgin green of early spring awakens the primordial spirit, dormant from the winter cold. "Plant, sow seeds, grow," it calls, "open yourself to the fullness of life."

Whether due to lack of sunlight or cabin fever, by the end of a long winter I'm usually a little blue. I fall asleep reading by the radiant heat of the wood stove, not from lack of sleep, but from lack of passion. But, passion returns with the opening of the elder flowers and the blossoming of the dandelions.

What glorious colors parade in the spring. The vibrant tulips give way to the delicate colors of some varieties of iris and the deep colors of others. The virgin green of the trees and bushes soon gives way to emerald. Our home, clearly visible from the road during winter, nestles in among the trees, almost hiding in the spring growth.

To the birdfeeder comes the Baltimore oriole, attracted by the orange halves I place there each morning. An indigo bunting darts to the feeder, perhaps seeking the millet. The bright yellow of the male goldfinch is striking next to the iridescent bunting. Soon the spectacular male rose-breasted grosbeak alights on the feeder, searching out the sunflower seeds. Sparrows, house finches, chickadees, and nuthatches put in their appearance before a blue jay spooks them back to the nearby branches.

Gardens, trees, and lawn, too, produce their colors of spring. The light green of leaf lettuce and of ferns contrasts with the black soil drenched by rain. The soft blue-green growth of the spruce and the delicate pink of the fragrant apple blossoms reveal themselves while the perfume of lilacs hangs in the air. Maral root, with its stunning crown of purple atop a three foot stem, adds its royal flair to the garden.

These vibrant colors of spring nourish my soul and stimulate the love for digging in the dirt to plant and to weed. Tenderly picking the weeds away from the wee carrots, onions, and beets takes the discernment and patience that spring calls forth.

Reflection on all life forms

A box elder tree is toppled in the wind
Life energy flows into the nothingness and the everyness,
Leaves and branches become soil to feed the grasses
And the grasses are eaten by the ruminants, which become the food of humans;

Soon spouts spring green from within the decaying trunk
Of that toppled box elder tree,
They thirst for the same cool rain and stretch toward the same warm sun
As did the branches now composting at its feet;

Wisdom finds existence
Through the double helix strands,
Yet more than singular DNA
Finds expression as an oak tree, a toad, a human being, an antelope or an oriole;

All sacred, all wise, all integral
To the beingness of one and the beingness of all,
Each form of life displaying purpose as an individual,
Yet interwoven in the living of the rest;

May we all remember to give honor
To each form of life we've seen or smelled or tasted on our tongues,
May we have awareness that each breath we take into our lungs
Belongs to all the other forms of life within and upon this hallowed ground;

To the tiny seed of carrot moist and warming in the sun
And the streaming seed of milkweed looking down upon the trees,
To the medicinal stinging nettle enlivening us from winter's cold,
And the earth worms in our soil whose worth is little understood;

Each time we smell *achillea's* pungency
Or hear the twittering of the wren,
Each time we touch an infant's smooth and silky skin
Or see a circling sprout of maize seed poke through the fertile ground,

May we wonder at this mystery that we call life
Ever marvel at its simplicity and complexity,
As we travel on the path toward the setting sun and the coming dawn
May we recall that I am you and you are all.

Dressing the dead

I struggled to make it through the motions of choosing a casket and making funeral arrangements. It all cost too much. There were polished metal caskets, some with softer padding and pillows than others, a mahogany casket, an oak one. We needed to buy a vault and work out the arrangements for the simple funeral we'd have at the mortuary.

Each item and service had a fee attached. John, along with Misty, our nineteen-year-old daughter, went through the motions with me. Jack Lynner, the funeral director, was pleasant enough and spoke softly, but I didn't want to be there. I hated the notion of caskets, and even more the notion of vaults. It wasn't death itself I hated so much, just the custom of burying people in those things.

I hoped a simple shroud would do for my own burial when it came. John wanted a simple pine box for his. But, JW wanted a casket, wanted to be buried in my family's cemetery plot. JW had gone into death the evening before, slipping away quietly as we held him.

I'm not sure that anyone is ready for death, especially not at seventeen. But, JW had known it was coming. He'd fought it and tried to hang onto life after the heart and double-lung transplant. He'd made it for almost two years. I'm sure some of that time was the best in his short life, but some had been torture as the breathing became more and more difficult, as his bony frame thinned more and more. Even while fighting against what he knew was coming, at another level JW had accepted it. He'd seen spirits calling him. He'd been soothed with the meditation tapes he listened to, especially those with my voice. As I'd comb his hair over and over or gently massage him, he would fall asleep. It had ended the previous evening when the breaths came farther and farther apart until there were none.

When we came to the funeral home, I carried a bag with JW's final dressing clothes. After we had chosen a mid-priced bronze-colored casket, I started to hand the clothes to Jack Lynner. "I noticed how comfortably you cared for him last night," said Jack. "Would you like to dress him?"

I hadn't considered dressing my son's body. I hadn't heard of others dressing their dead. "Yes," I said without hesitation. Although I wouldn't have thought of doing it, the idea felt right, felt good.

I followed Jack down the hall into an elevator. When we got out, he said, "My wife washed his hair last night and bathed him. He's naked now. If you brought underwear, I'll put on his shorts before you come in." I reached in the bag and handed him the shorts.

I waited until he beckoned me.

I entered the cool room. JW lay on a table on his back, his head held up by metal tubing. His rose quartz crystal laid above his heart, the only adornment apart from his turquoise shorts. His hair was brushed straight back. Oscar, a stuffed harp seal he had loved, laid on his shoulder and upper chest.

His body was fairly rigid, but would bend with some pressure. My taped meditation was playing. I had asked Mr. Lynner to play the tape for JW while he waited for his funeral. I pulled on the light blue jeans that Mom and Pops had given him. I put on John's brightly colored shirt that JW had loved. I buttoned it and pulled the bright pink sweater I had bought just that morning over his head. I talked to JW as I dressed him as I had done in caring for him the past several months, softly. I told him about the Yankee Country candle that still burned at home, the candle that we'd burned constantly the previous few weeks.

Jack put in JW's blue lapis earring and shaved him. I combed his almost black hair, letting it fall gently over his forehead.

He looked beautiful. I knew that it was his beautiful, frail body that I dressed; yet while the body was his, I knew that he was not simply his body.

I felt warm and strong. Dressing him comforted me, as I had not been comforted earlier by words of caring, of sympathy, of love. I felt peaceful, pensive, but not sad. I had a sensation of knowing that JW was woven into me, that there was no real separation between us.

Jack Lynner and I carried him to the casket and gently laid him in. Then I re-arranged his sweater and hair. I positioned Oscar in JW's hands so that the toy seal looked up at his face.

We took the elevator to where John and Misty waited. They each spent several minutes with him, each shedding tears from time to time. John, and then Misty, each kissed his cheek. We left for home, to let others know of the funeral plan, to prepare for the evening when family would join us to spend time near JW.

Years passed. My favorite aunt died.

I dressed her for her funeral, as I had JW. I curled her hair using bobby pins to make pin curls like she used to do, and later combed it in the fashion she wore, not like beauty parlour fixing. I stretched a string of pearls around her neck.

It was different dressing Aunt Elynor than it had been with JW, perhaps partly because she had been reasonably healthy until her sudden death, so I hadn't cared for her in the same personal way I had cared for JW. When Jack Lynner had asked if I wanted to dress JW, I felt called to do so, called without question. With Elynor, such a private lady, I simply believed she would not like to be dressed by a stranger. She'd disliked doctors examining her body.

I told the funeral director what I wanted to do. He seemed surprised and somewhat uncomfortable with the idea, but I persuaded him I could do it, that I wanted to do it.

Like dressing JW, dressing Elynor felt right. It gave me a personal, close time to say things I may have never said in life, but should have. It eased a little of my sadness and self-reproach over having not persuaded her to see a doctor, but it would take a nighttime dream-state visit from my long-deceased grandmother a week or so later to erase the pangs of guilt.

I'm not sure if a spiritual part of JW and of Elynor were still present while I dressed them, but I talked with each of them as if they were there. I don't know if a spiritual self hovered close and paid attention and appreciated this final act of caring. I simply know that I felt close to each of them, felt interwoven with them as I put on their clothes and combed their hair.

I'm thankful to Jack Lynner for suggesting I dress JW. Our cultural fear of death too often distances us from personal contact with death and from final acts necessary for our own healthy grieving.

A shroud or a casket

Whether I am buried in a simple cotton shroud or in an eight thousand dollar casket, I will return to earth. My body may skeletonize within months in a shroud. In a metal casket, my own bacteria will likely eat away my flesh before the maggots devour me. It may take years, but my body will rot. Eventually, even the steel casket and the concrete vault will break down and return to dust.

The funeral industry has convinced most people that embalming, expensive caskets, sealed vaults, and other funeral paraphernalia are necessary for proper burial. The impossible dream of retaining our bodies feeds our willingness to believe that embalming will preserve us. It doesn't. Nor do sealed caskets. Vaults don't keep "the worms" away forever either. Sealing off a body from the elements actually hastens putrefaction from internal anaerobic bacteria.

At a time when emotion rules reason, grieving family members spend an average of seven thousand dollars to bury their dead.

Humans have buried their dead for at least fifty thousand years. Mummification or burial in a particular type of boggy soil or the dry sands of deserts preserved hundreds or thousands of bodies. Many of these ancient bodies have the dubious honor or being displayed thousands of years after the flow of blood and breath within them ceased. Billions of other bodies have been recycled as fertilizer for other life forms. A few others have had parts of their bodies plasticized, clearly showing the anatomy of muscles, or nervous system or kidneys, and been on display in the Body Worlds exhibit.

My plea is to bury me wrapped in a shroud beneath an old tree. If that won't do, cremation and then burial by a big tree will be fine. Let me be resurrected in a leaf or a blade of grass. I'm connected with all of nature through millennia of recycling of the dead. My death will simply complete one cycle and start anew.

We twenty-first century humans find it hard to talk about death. Discussing what happens to our bodies after death is even more difficult. So, we take the easy route and let the professionals tell us what to do. Believing that embalming is essential, we create a "memory picture" of our loved ones by allowing the mortician to slice the skin and muscles, drain the blood, pump chemicals into the arteries and poke them into the abdomen, pack the orifices, mold the face with putty, and paint the skin with actor's cosmetics. Some of us spend our meager lifetime savings on costly funerals because we have forgotten our connection with nature.

All known cultures have had ceremonies commemorating their dead. Most cultures have afforded the rich man more extravagant measures to preserve the body for a few years longer than the poor man or woman. Yet, rich and poor alike return to earth after burning or decaying.

I expect I'll walk and breathe and write for many years to come, but someday—or some night—I will die. Whether I die rich or poor, I prefer that my body quickly returns to earth. After my friends and relatives wrap my corpse in a shroud and lower it into a hand-dug grave or help load it into a crematorium, I hope they have a ceremony to share my joy. The critters, the insects, or the plants can feed on my weary body as I embark on a spiritual adventure that harmonizes with notes in a different dimension.

Chokecherry

Small deciduous tree

Prized for making jellies, wines, and syrups, chokecherries are especially astringent, so not very palatable until sweetened. Like its cousin, the wild black cherry *(Prunus serotina),* chokecherry bark has medicinal qualities and has been used in making cough syrups. It has antitussive, sedative, antibacterial, and antiviral effects. It improves digestion and has a soothing effect on the gastric mucosa.

The chokecherry tree normally grows ten or more feet high and can reach significantly higher. It produces white flowers in racemes in the spring, followed by reddish fruit in late summer.

The bark is collected in summer, which is unusual since most bark is collected in the winter. Make a decoction or tincture or use tinctured bark, along with the fruit, to make a cough syrup. The fruit, of course, is used for jellies, syrups, and pies.

Cleavers (goosegrass, bedstraw)

Gallium apartine
Perennial

Cleavers is a tonic for the lymphatic system, so is useful for swollen glands, especially around the neck or ears. It has mild diuretic, laxative, and astringent properties. It is especially good for acute inflammation in the urinary system. It lowers blood pressure, is alterative, and has detoxifying and reputed slimming effects. Cleavers is used internally for chronic fatigue, mononucleosis, cystitis, eczema, and psoriasis. Externally, it is used for skin irritations. Juice of fresh cleavers tightens the skin, so makes a good facial. Gargling with bedstraw helps ease constriction of the vocal cords. Treben promoted its use for darkened, roughened areas of the skin, along with calendula, nettle, and yarrow. She also touted its use for serious kidney disorders, especially when mixed with equal parts of goldenrod and nettle. "The tea is taken on an empty stomach thirty minutes before breakfast and three to four more cups through the day," she wrote. In old times, bedstraw was used as a bed for giving birth.

Cleavers is a scrambling, climbing plant that sticks to anything nearby. It has whorls of small elliptical leaves with tiny white flowers. The stem is covered with little hooked bristles that fasten themselves to plants, fences, or whatever is near.

Use the fresh whole herb, including the aerial parts and seeds, in infusions, tinctures, or juice. It loses much of its healing value upon drying.

Columbine
Aquilegia canadensis
Perennial

An astringent herb, columbine balances body fluids. It is a reputed love charm and the seeds rubbed into hair help get rid of lice. The leaves have been used for sores in the mouth and throat and the seeds for liver problems. Columbine, however, is seldom used today as a medicinal herb, but rather grown as a showy garden plant.

Columbine grows one to two feet high with a loose head of drooping flowers. Wild columbine has red and yellow flowers. Many cultivars in various colors are available. The whole plant—leaves, flowers, and root—is mildly medicinal and is used dried or tinctured.

Comfrey
Symphytum officinale
Perennial

Comfrey stimulates growth when the system is having trouble regenerating itself. It assists in bone repair and is used for chronic coughs due to worn down cilia, as from smoking. It is considered a specific for decreased bone density in the lower spine and for healing internal ulcers. There are, however, some alkaloids in the root which have been linked to liver tumors, so it should be used cautiously and for only short periods. For bone repair, it can be used externally as well as internally. Comfrey causes tissue to heal extremely well, so is good for superficial wounds. However, because it can cause the tissue to heal on the outside before internal healing is complete, it should not be used on deep wounds. The root is mucilaginous and nutritive. The leaves, scalded and used as a poultice, help heal sprains. A poultice made from the tincture of comfrey root will also aid in the healing of wounds, bone fractures, and other injuries.

The plant grows five or more feet high, with huge rough leaves and produces pink/purple flowers that are often visited by bumble bees. It is invasive through root growth and difficult to fully remove from the garden, so it is best to plant it in a space separate from the rest of the garden.

Among the ten virtues Gerard listed for comfrey are: "The rootes of comfrey, ftamped and the juice drunke with wine, helpeth thofe that fpit bloud and healeth all inward wounds and burftings. The fame bruifed and laid in a manner of a plaifter, doth heale all frefh and greene woundes, and are so glutenatiue that it will fodder or glew together meate that is chopt in peeces feething in a pot and maketh it in one lumpe." (The roots of comfrey, stamped and the juice drunk with wine, help those that spit blood and heal all inward wounds and burstings. The same bruised and laid in a manner of a plaster heals all fresh and green wounds and are so glutenative that it will sodder or glue together meat that is chopped in pieces seething in a pot and make it into one lump.)

Harvest the root and use fresh for tincture or cold infusion—by soaking the root for several hours in cold water—or dry for later use. The leaves can be used for tisanes. In addition, use fresh or dried root to make an infused oil.

Coneflower, purple (narrow leaved) *Echinacea angustifolia*
Perennial

This herb has been widely promoted as an immune stimulant, which it is. However, as a stimulant, not a tonic, it should be used only at the beginning and during infections or for short times—not routinely. *Echinacea* is one of the most effective stimulant detoxifiers for the circulatory, lymphatic, and respiratory systems. The Plains Tribes of Native Americans regarded *Echinacea angustifolia* as a cure-all.

Echinacea angustifolia is a native prairie plant, growing readily in rich, well drained alkaline soil in the sun. The cultivar *E. purpurea* is easier to grow and has a showier flower, but is not as medicinally active.

Roots from four-year-old or older plants are harvested, but harvesting in the wild should be avoided because *Echinacea* has been over harvested, so is endangered. The root can be used fresh for tincture or dried for decoction.

Corn silk *Zea mays*
Annual

An old American Indian remedy for cystitis or bladder inflammation, corn silk is the female part of the corn plant that collects the pollen. Each silk, if pollinated, has the potential of developing a kernel of corn. It is sweet, demulcent, healing, and soothing to the urinary tract and to irritated intestinal mucosa. Corn silk has been used for divination and in casting spells. The silk is diuretic due to its high concentration of potassium. It also lowers blood sugar and helps prevent formation of urinary stones.

Corn is an annual that is planted as a garden vegetable or field crop. Ancient varieties were planted in South and Central America over five thousand years ago.

Gather when corn is silking in early summer before it begins to dry. Tincture fresh or dry for tisanes.

Cranesbill (wild geranium)

Geranimum maculatum
Perennial

Wild geranium is a magical herb that benefits persons who have lost part of their soul (Wood). Use is also advised when there is too much mucus in the lungs, stool, or urine as well as for chronic diarrhea. It is highly astringent and antiseptic and helps stop bleeding, such as uterine and post partum hemorrhage. It is used externally to treat wounds and was widely used by Native Americans for that purpose. It can also be juiced with some water to make a facial that closes the pores, tightening the skin.

Cranesbill grows one to two feet high and has deeply toothed palmate leaves and pink-purple saucer shaped flowers that appear in spring to early summer, followed by beaked seed-pods. It is native to eastern North America.

Use the roots collected in the autumn and the leaves collected in summer for tincture or the fresh or dried roots for decoction.

Dandelion

Taraxacum officinale
Perennial

All parts of the dandelion are useful. The flowers are edible and make a good wine. The leaves are an excellent diuretic. The root is one of the best remedies for chronic or intermittent liver problems. Dandelion stimulates the liver into more effective functioning. It likely stimulates the kidneys to function better as well. Often people who need dandelion have a slightly yellow complexion and yellowish sclera of the eye. Dandelion root is sometimes employed to remove gallstones, but must be taken over

44

a period of months to achieve this effect.

Dandelion is a pervasive weed of lawns and almost anywhere else with soil. It has a bright yellow flower in a rosette of leaves.

Among other things, Gerard wrote of dandelion, " The juice drunke is good againſt the vnuoluntary effuſion of the feed" (The juice drunk is good against the involuntary effusion of the seed—that is, sperm.) He adds, "a decoction made of the whole plant helps the yellow jaundice."

Leaves are best gathered in the spring. The root should be collected in the fall. Both can be tinctured. Leaves can be dried for use in a tisane or used fresh in a salad. The roots are used in decoction or tincture—either fresh or dried.

Elecampane

Inula helenium
Perennial

Elecampane is expectorant, anti-inflammatory, diuretic and antispasmotic. It increases perspiration and is effective against bacteria and fungi. It is indicated for acute bronchitis and asthma, especially in children. Elecampane is useful whenever excess mucus causes indigestion. It can also be used externally on infected cuts. Elecampane is a bitter, pungent herb that acts as an alterative, eliminating toxins, stimulating the immune and digestive systems, and helping to expel intestinal parasites. The flower also yields yellow and orange dyes. The root has been used in making cordials and as a flavoring for puddings.

Elecampane is a huge plant, native to Europe and western Asia. It grows about six feet tall and displays immense leaves and large yellow flowers, producing an attractive and unusual backdrop to a garden. It grows well in most soils and likes clay. It needs a good deal of water to flourish.

In Ancient Rome, the herbalist Pliny regarded this herb as an antidote to poisons and the herbalist Dioscorides used it to treat snake bite. In the sixteenth and seventeenth centuries, both Culpeper and Gerard used it for chest complaints.

Harvest the root in fall just at dormancy (European tradition) and harvest the flowers in bloom (Chinese tradition). The roots can be divided without killing the plant. Use the root fresh for tincture or dry for decoction.

Making an herbal tincture

Herbal tinctures develop when an herb is soaked in a clear alcohol such as white brandy or vodka. The constituents of most herbs readily extract into the alcohol. Some herbs, however, are used only as a tisane or decoction because one or more of elements do not extract well; others are used primarily as an oil or ointment, applied externally. Most tinctures are best made using fresh herbs, but can be made with dried herbs (and a few require dried herbs). Although vinegar can be used as the extracting medium, the herbs are best preserved in alcohol. Most commonly, the medicinal tincture dose is just a few drops either placed directly in the mouth or ingested with water or other liquid. An alcoholic tincture will preserve the herb for years.

An herbal tincture requires an alcohol that is at least twenty-five percent pure. Most alcohols, such as brandy or vodka, are thirty-five to forty percent. Such alcohols can be diluted slightly to make the tincture and there are formulas for doing so. For personal and non-commercial use, however, this offers no advantage. The tincture produced with these higher alcohol concentrations will be slightly stronger than most commercially sold.

Herbal tinctures are easy to make. The following "rule of thumb" gives an easy, not very scientific, guideline to proportions and soaking time for various herbal parts. While you can find books and articles that give exact proportions in weight, for personal use such scientific precision is not necessary.

RULE OF THUMB FOR PROPORTIONS AND SOAKING TIMES

Fresh aerial parts:

To tincture fresh aerial parts such as flowers, leaves, and stems, chop the herbs into small pieces, unless using a small herb such as St. John's wort or chamomile flowers. Fill a jar with the parts loosely packed. Barely cover the herb with the alcohol. Soak for one week or so, rocking the jar back and forth once or twice a day. Strain the alcohol from the herb, ideally using milk filters available at farm stores or, alternatively, cheesecloth. Discard the herb into your compost heap. Put the alcoholic tincture in a bottle (ideally a dark one) and place out of direct sunlight. Be sure to label, including the year.

Dried aerial parts:

Put the herb in a jar, again loosely packed, letting the herb settle itself. Note how high the herb is in the jar. Cover the herb with alcohol using twice the volume of alcohol as the herb, so that the jar will have alcohol twice as high as the herb was alone. Soak for about two weeks. Strain as above.

Roots and barks:

Put the fresh or dried roots or bark in the jar. Use three times the volume of alcohol as plant material, so the alcohol will fill the jar two times higher than the herb was by itself. Soak for three weeks to one month. Strain as above.

Playing Out-of-doors

When I was a child a winter Saturday meant adventure. Sledding, ice skating, building igloos, and making snowmen were among my pursuits, although perhaps I should have made snowwomen. My friends and I even went "wibber lubbing," which was our made-up name meaning *river loving*. We'd walk on the ice and through the culverts of the creek in Chinhinta Park pretending to be explorers in the untamed West. I remember falling through the ice and getting soaked to my thighs. I ran home—a few blocks—and my mom wrapped me in a Hudson Bay blanket and served me hot chocolate.

In the summer, my friends and I knit hot pads and made other simple crafts. We gathered our old toys and Cracker Jack prizes and had backyard sales, complete with lemonade for sale. Swimming in the outside pool took up many hot afternoons. In the evening we'd play *Annie Annie over* and holler "pigtails" if the ball didn't make it over the house. Hide and seek and blind man's bluff were other favorites.

Whether it was climbing trees, bicycling, looking for frogs, or finding four-leaf clovers, outside play almost always included some adventure or make-believe. There were times, too, when making paper dolls and playing indoor games such as Uncle Wiggly and Monopoly were afternoon activities. If the weather was good, however, outside play was always the best. We'd walk a mile or so to "The Rocks," a granite outcropping, and spend hours there making believe we were Indians or early settlers. I also remember creating a circus to present to other kids. One of the events was supposed to be having my friend's dad drive his car over me while I lay flat on the ground. He declined the opportunity. Other times we spent hours learning "ob language," which I can still speak fluently, to be able to keep secrets from our folks or siblings.

I remember occasionally telling my mom, "There is nothing to do." Her response was usually, "Spit in your shoe and give it to your teacher at half past two." We'd find something else to do.

Today, I drive through neighborhoods in the summer, neighborhoods where I know children live, evidenced by bicycles and other trappings of childhood. Often I don't even see one child playing out-of-doors on a nice summer day. It is even rarer to see children out playing in the winter snow.

Both children and society are suffering. Adventurous make-believe play with minimal adult supervision fosters development of social skills and cooperation. Fights sometimes develop in such play and children get injured physically or emotionally, but the reality of such interactions teaches children better ways to interact and gradually introduces them to the risks inherent in some activities. Minimally supervised outdoor play also satisfies a primal desire for adventure. Perhaps the lack of real adventure for many children of today leads to less healthy attempts to bring risk into their lives when they have the chance.

It might be that some positive values develop when TV and video-viewing and electronic games take precedence over out-of-doors play. But, if so, my age and memory cloud my ability to see them.

Que Sera Sera

On a Saturday morning while driving to the home of a friend who lives on Green Lake near Spicer, I listened to Minnesota Public Radio. Scott Simon was interviewing Ray Evans, part of the songwriting team of Livingston and Evans that created the song, "Que Sera Sera" first sung by Doris Day fifty years ago. Hearing the song brought memories.

No longer was I hearing re-runs of President Bush's State of the Union address, with calls for war with Iraq growing stronger. I was nine-years-old again, spending a summer week with my friend, Carolie, whose family had a cottage on Green Lake near the Old Mill Inn. During that week, along with swimming, croquet, badminton, and card games, we'd dream about future marriages and would look through Bride Magazine to plan our weddings. We'd sing the popular songs of the era, and at the time one of them was "Que Sera Sera." We'd play in the sand and make castles and imagine our own castles of the future. Mrs. Owens, Carolie's mom, would read a chapter of *The Adventures of Tom Sawyer* or *Alice's Adventures in Wonderland*. Each year I visited, Carolie and I would make up a musical play to present to our mothers when my mom would come to pick me up.

I don't remember the content of the plays we created, but one play included "Que sera sera, whatever will be will be." We dressed in costumes and danced with a fluidity that lacked the inhibitions of my later years. We wove our dreams into the stories of movie stars and teachers and moms and dads. Our moms would applaud and applaud some more.

On that Saturday morning in January, 2003, I felt eight-years-old, yet fifty-eight. I hungered for that time of innocence when the adults in my world took care of me, when dreams were all ahead of me, when the human beingness of childhood was not resigned to the human doingness of my later years, when the weight of adult decisions did not enter the photograph of my dreams. On that morning, I missed my childhood sister-like friendship that had lacked all pretenses. I missed my friend's mom, whom I often called my "other mother." Especially I missed my mom, dead over two years, the easy conversations we would have in that time, the comfort of her always being around as a fifties stay-at-home woman, and the smell of bread baking mingled with oatmeal-raisin cookies we called "rocks."

I'm not a woman who tears or cries easily, and most commonly when tears do come, they are stimulated by seeing an animal hurt or a bird devoured by a cat. But, the tears flowed that Saturday morning as the years evaporated while my car moved toward Green Lake. "I asked my mother, what will I be? Will I be pretty, will I be rich?"

Will I have children, I wondered back then—and I did. Would I be rich? Well, yes, in comparison to most citizens of the world. Were there rainbows day after day? No, but there have been literal rainbows that arched across the wide prairie sky and, like hearing "Que Sera Sera," created a childhood sense of joy. And there have been allegorical ones that brightened dismal days.

I wonder if children of today pretend the way we did fifty years ago. I wonder if many of them still have trunks of old clothes to don in their make-believe world. I wonder if the commercialism of the twenty-first century has forever erased that sense of innocence I felt back then—or is my concern just the pattern of an older generation forever looking back on a world that seemed less flawed?

No ice cream cone

A memory starting in childhood

Mom was driving the old green Studebaker and telling me one of her stories about Putsky-Nutsky. This was Mom's name for an eccentric old woman who lived in a tin house near her childhood home. "I was about your age," she said, "when neighbor girls and I got dressed up for Halloween. We gathered some stones, ran down the hill to Putsky-Nutsky's place, and began pelting them onto her tin roof. When Putsky came tearing out of her house, I began running, then tripped on my ghost costume. Struggling, I ripped off my disguise while Putsky-Nutsky's shouting came nearer. Leaving my costume on the ground, I ran toward home and never looked back."

Mom had taken me to the swimming pool and I'd dived off the high board that evening, showing off my new skill. Afterwards, she and I headed for Art's Dairy Freeze where a nickel cone would top off a fine summer evening. Mmmmm … I imagined the taste of creamy chocolate, soft and smooth.

Just as we pulled into Art's, Mom went pale and let out a gasp. Looking straight ahead and saying nothing to me, she circled the driveway around the Dairy Freeze and turned back toward home. I wondered if she had just become ill. I'd once overheard my friend's mom tell mine that she was going to have a heart attack if she kept working so hard. *Was she going to die?* I wondered.

Mom sat up straight in the seat with her eyes glued to the road. I looked out the front window, too, glancing at Mom out of the corner of my eye from time to time. After a few minutes, I asked tentatively, "What's wrong?"

Silence for two blocks.

"I didn't ever want to tell you about him," she began. "My first husband. He must be out of prison. He was at the Diary Freeze."

You were married before? I wanted to blurt out. *To a man who's been in jail?* But I kept quiet.

Mom kept looking straight ahead as we approached our house.

I sat there, struggling with the thoughts that surfaced. *Mom's been divorced.* That had been a condition I'd reserved for movie stars. *Why did the man go to jail? Does Daddy know?*

Mom parked in front of the house, but kept looking out the window, not moving to get out of the car. "He was sent to prison a few years back after he raped a girl," she said. I heard a quiver in her voice. I looked at her then. I noticed her eyelids were twitching. At nine-years-old, I had a vague notion of what rape meant, but it wasn't clear. I knew it had something to do with sex and was evil. I started shaking inside.

"Are you scared of him?" I asked.

She nodded.

After a few more moments of silence, she added, "Mostly I'm afraid for you girls."

I didn't know what to say to that. I wondered if I should be afraid, but I was too shocked to be scared.

"Don't ever, ever, ever get into a car with someone you don't know."

"No, I won't," I said, glad to offer something to ease her nervousness. "I never would."

Months, even a year passed. I recalled the incident, but didn't hear more about this former husband. I thought about asking my grandmother about him, but never did. Mom didn't tell me not to ask about him, but she must have given some indication that I shouldn't. Sometimes I wondered if this man really existed and if what Mom had said were true. No man ever offered me a ride.

I was aware, however, of a change in Mom's demeanor that began after that incident. I'd notice her starring into the distance, a gloomy look on her face. She was not generally given to bickering, but I'd hear her complaining to Daddy. I'd often find her resting on the couch when I came home from school. I heard her talking on the phone to the school principal about changing the teacher my brother was scheduled to have. "He can't have a woman like that for a teacher," she said. "I couldn't stand him having a teacher who is married to that awful man." I assumed that her former husband was married to this teacher, but I found it hard to believe that someone who had raped a girl would be married to a teacher.

Another time I heard Mom talking on the phone to an attorney, the dad of a friend of mine. "But there has to be something they can do. Does he have to rape someone or maybe kill me to keep him away?" she lamented.

I'd hear her coughing in the morning, a cough that was new. Yet, most of life went on as it had. She still baked bread every week. Clothes were washed and ironed, the house was always clean. She'd bring Daddy his noon and supper meals at the gas station he owned and ran by himself.

I felt a new care-taking role emerging in me. Mom didn't ask for my help, but I sensed some message that I must try to ease her sadness.

I set about my new job. I'd tell humorous stories to try to make her laugh. She'd almost always laugh when laughter was expected, but it was a "tee hee" kind of laugh, not the giggle I had known. I stopped hanging around with girls Mom called "wild" and I resumed my friendship with the doctor's daughter, approved of by Mom. I studied hard at school. *Maybe getting straight A's would make her happy.* I practiced the piano when I was supposed to and did dishes with mom almost every night, even nights when it was my sister's turn.

A couple years later, about the time I entered high school, I started to think of Mom as neurotic, as stupidly afraid of nothing. She believed people at our church were gossiping about her, that one of her friends was shunning her, that the neighbors didn't want to have coffee with her anymore. She went to a doctor because of the chronic cough and he referred her to a neurologist in Minneapolis. She confused neurologist with psychiatrist, I think, and got mad at the doctor for thinking she was nuts.

I still didn't ask her about her former husband. It was one of those things, like my dad's occasional binge drinking, which seemed to be a secret. I wondered if any of my friends knew and even felt embarrassed about having a Mom that had been divorced and married to a man who had been in prison.

While I lived at home, I never learned the name of the man who was her former husband and was never offered a ride by a stranger. Occasionally, when I was near the end of high school and when Mom and I were alone, she'd say a few things about him. "The night before our divorce, he held a gun to my head and forced me," she said—not exactly explaining what he forced her to do, but by then I understood. She also said, "I didn't get gonorrhea from him. I couldn't have because I had four children." I didn't know much about gonorrhea, but accepted her explanation without questioning her. She told me she had been pregnant by him once and he had thrown her down the stairs and caused a miscarriage.

Mom's statements gave me a glimpse into a marriage she had entered at age sixteen and left at nineteen, but never revealed a clear picture.

I entered nursing school at the University of Minnesota. In my first nursing class I was asked why I wanted to be a nurse. "Because there's a lot of pain in the world and I want to diminish that pain," I said.

When I was twenty-five and living in Minneapolis, Mom had what was called a nervous breakdown. It was a year after my dad died. She had stayed to herself most of that year, venturing out for groceries and perhaps to go to church, but not for fun. I called her once a week during that year. She usually sounded cheerful enough on the phone, but it became clear to me that she wasn't seeing any friends, again believing they didn't like her. My sister, Sue, who lived in a nearby town, visited Mom at least once a week. As the year progressed Sue and I had several phone conversations about Mom and our worry about her mental health, but neither of us knew what to do.

Near the end of that year, Sue called to tell me that Mom had told her that someone on the radio had proposed to her. That jolted me. This wasn't just depression. Mom was getting crazy. I left for home a few hours later. When I got home, Mom was giddy. She exuded the happiness I remembered her expressing when I was a child, but the effervescence seemed inappropriate. Changing to a fearful voice, Mom said as if telling me a secret, "My former husband is watching me, you know." By then, my aunt had told me his name and verified that he still lived in our hometown.

The next day Mom made me take her to a doctor to check her for gonorrhea.

I sat in the waiting room. I was both embarrassed and deeply worried. I didn't believe she had gonorrhea, but wondered what stuff existed in her head that allowed her to overcome what I would have expected to be her own embarrassment about going to a doctor about gonorrhea when she was sixty-years-old. I recognized that Mom must have sexual fears hidden deeply within her. *Had her former husband raped her recently?* I wondered. *Does this all stem from some abuse in her childhood? Her father? Her weird older brother who played the mandolin? How abusive was her former husband?*

When she got the results of the test, she was so relieved that she called a couple of friends to tell them that her test for VD was negative. Again I felt embarrassed—more for her than for me.

A week later my sister Sue and I got together with our brother Doug at his place. We swapped stories about Mom's weird behavior. Since I was the nurse in the family, Sue and Doug expected me to know what to do—or maybe I just expected it of myself. Finally I said, "Let's go see her. I'll simply be straight with her. We can sit here and talk about her, but she needs to know we'll try to understand and that we love her."

I fidgeted on the way there. In my mind I played over possible ways of starting the conversation. *You know, Mom you don't seem quite right these days. ... Mom, we all love you and we're concerned. ... Mom, I'm not sure what to say, but you're acting kind of strange. ...*

When the three of us walked in, Mom was just finishing baking some fancy cookies called lemon cups, "Oh, good, you've come for coffee," she said, "How good to have you all together. It's been awhile, hasn't it?" *Like years, except for holidays,* I wanted to say. "I made some cookies, "she said, "and I don't want to eat any. I've got to lose weight for the wedding," she said, with a strange smile.

"Coffee and cookies would be nice," I said. We siblings gathered around the table as Mom went to get cups. We looked at each other as if to say, "Off da…what do we do now?"

When Mom sat down, my throat was dry and I took a couple of sips of coffee before I began. "Mom, we are all concerned about you. You're telling us that you're going to be married and it doesn't make sense." I looked her straight in the eyes. Her eyes flickered in the nystagmus way I had noticed earlier. Her smile evaporated.

My eyes left hers and I took another sip of coffee for strength. "The thing about the radio, Mom. People don't propose marriage over the radio."

She looked me in the eyes again, then looked away, "But I heard him" she said with a plaintiff sound in her voice.

"I know," I said. "I'm sure you believe you heard him."

Tears welled in my eyes, "Mom, sometimes when we are so lonely, we hear the things we want to hear." I reached across the table and took her hand in mine. Tears formed in her eyes, too, and she was silent for some moments.

I waited for some words from her, finding it hard to come up with words of my own.

Sue said, "We want to help. We love you and we don't know what to do."

"Nobody likes me anymore except you kids," Mom said.

Something had changed in her demeanor. I sensed that reality had broken through her fantasy. I dared to ask, "Do you really believe you are going to get married, Mom?"

"I suppose not," she said. "Sometimes I do. Other times it seems kind of crazy. I can't quite figure out who it is that wants to marry me."

I felt relieved that her hallucinations weren't so firmly entrenched that she couldn't deny them. "Oh Mom, I'm sure it seems pretty nice to think about happy things like marriage, but it's not real, you know." I spoke slowly looking at her even though she wasn't looking at me.

Then she looked up. "Well, how about some more coffee?"

She didn't wait for a response, just got up and got the pot and started filling cups.

Mom asked how my son Greg was doing and I said he was doing fine. "And how is your job going?"

"Very good," I said.

We all talked about normal family things for a few more minutes while I wished I didn't have to approach her craziness again.

"I want you to get some help, Mom—see friends, see a doctor or a nurse."

"I'm not going to see a doctor," she said firmly.

"Okay. But I can't stay here and none of us can stay here and I need to know that you are all right. Your mind really isn't working quite right. … Would it be okay if I contacted a public health nurse, like I am, to come and see you once a week or so?"

"I guess so," she said.

"I'll arrange it then," I said.

Again the conversation drifted to ordinary events. A short while later, Sue and Doug left. I made the referral to the public health nurse and then spent the evening with Mom. Her behavior alternated between normal and bizarre. I stopped to see my brother and sister before I left for home the next day. They each agreed to visit Mom often and let me know how things were going.

The public health nurse referred Mom to a Homemaker's Club to ensure some social contact, and later referred her to a psychiatrist and even drove her to the clinic. The psychiatrist recommended inpatient treatment.

Mom entered a psychiatric unit on a Thursday, a day before a huge winter storm. On Saturday, the day after the storm, I drove a hundred miles, plowed through snowdrifts a couple of feet high, to see her in the hospital. I refused to allow shock treatment, which the doctor recommended. I told the doctor about the sexual things Mom had mentioned to me and encouraged him to help Mom talk through those things.

She remained hospitalized just a couple of weeks, took some anti-psychotic pills for a few months, attended a support group, and received follow–up visits from the nurse. Gradually she improved and started making regular social contacts.

Not long after her hospitalization, Doug saw Mom's former husband sitting in front of her house in his car. Doug recognized the guy because one of his friends had pointed him out at a restaurant a few years earlier. The guy's name was Ernie, like my dad's. Ernie left when he saw my brother. That was the first confirmation we had of his harassment of Mom. Doug called the police. When I learned of the incident I felt guilty about my years of not believing Mom about his harassment.

Mom remarried a few years later and I was glad she'd no longer be alone, relieved that she'd have someone to look after her and love her. Her new husband was an ethical man, a generous man. He was, until he and Mom married, a Norwegian bachelor farmer, and his name, too, was Ernie. He later told me that when he and Mom were dating, he'd called the sheriff about the other Ernie. The stalking stopped.

When Mom was seventy-two, she called me one evening to tell me that her former husband had died. She still didn't use his name. "I don't have to wonder about him anymore," she said with an easiness in her voice that likely reflected the relief gurgling up from her soul.

After that, Mom had occasional spells we kids would call her "funny times," when she would suggest that people were talking about her behind her back, or calling her and hanging up. Her interpretation of people's motivations sometimes seemed strange and paranoid, but she lived a reasonably happy life into her late eighties. Her laughter returned and she and I giggled sometimes like we did when I was a kid. She shared twenty-one good years of marriage with her third Ernie.

Reflecting upon that period of time about a year after Daddy died, I've considered that what looked like crazy behavior could actually have been a necessary, even healthy, response. Mom had withdrawn into her own private world with curtains closed and the world blocked out. She was filled with fear and sadness. Then, as if a switch were flipped, she would hear voices coming through the radio—voices of love, a marriage proposal, and sounds of gaiety. She had replaced her drawn look of woe with smiles. Giggles bubbled forth in a geyser from a mirthful wellspring within her. She appeared happier than I had seen her since I was a child.

Although doctors diagnosed her behavior as a psychotic break, I believe it was my mother's way of letting go of grief and getting beyond despair. She needed the outlet called insanity for a brief moment of her life as an antidote to her fear and loneliness.

She also needed to know that her fear of harassment wasn't some paranoid delusion, but a real threat. I regret that it took so many years for me to learn that.

Memories of a Sunday dinner

Reflections of my mom come to mind while I gaze down upon gulf waters on our approach to the Sarasota, Florida airport. I remember a photo of her at age sixteen with a softness to her beauty, just a hint of a smile and a serious expression I don't see in present day youth. I envision Mom from my early childhood with her striking dark auburn curly hair framing her face, making her face appear diminutive. I recall Mom of my teenage years—her large frame heavier then—with a stiffness to her expression and to her stride, then again at seventy-five with a softness having returned to her face, along with an easy smile, but with her body moving as if the muscles were too tightly strung.

The plane lands. I retrieve my bags, arrange for a rented car, and maneuver through unfamiliar traffic to my folks' condominium, one of those places where they don't allow kids and dogs.

There she is coming toward me as I exit the car. With a wide smile, she attempts a fast pace, holding her arms stiffly, bent at the elbows, swinging them back and forth as if agitating the wash.

Mom puckers her lips for a brief kiss. We hug and exchange words of welcome, of happiness to be once again together.

She nears her eighty-fourth birthday and looks old now. Although her face is not wrinkled, it is pasty with the pallor of age. Her cheeks sag like a mushroom just starting to soften. The eyes, once sparkling, are clouded with cataracts and pinpricks of brown spot the green irises. Her smile reveals deep crevices and her lipstick, too bright, is not quite evenly applied. Her once shiny auburn hair is now nearly white, yet still attractive.

She has dressed up for my coming. She wears pull-on red pants that bulge a bit below her waist, a beige silky shirt with a lacy collar, and a red jacket, just a slight shade off from that of the pants.

As we walk toward the condo, I notice that Mom's left hip clicks and her back rounds toward her slim shoulders.

Inside, the table is set with Mom's blue and white English Village china. Candles burn in brass candlesticks surrounded by dangling crystals. Mom has arranged a fruit salad, looking like a picture in Ladies Home Journal, and placed it near each dinner plate. The aroma coming from the kitchen calls forth memories of childhood Sunday dinners.

While age has changed Mom's appearance, what is unchanged is her delight in having her family visit, her skill in preparing delicious food, and her artistic flair in presenting the dinner.

Elder

Both stimulant and sedative, the flowers and berries of *Sambucus canendensis* open the pores of the skin to diminish fevers and clean the respiratory channels, colon, and kidneys. It is useful for all the tubes of the body (Wood). It is a detoxifying diuretic with antiviral and antispasmotic qualities. An elderberry syrup is made by boiling the berries, adding honey, cinnamon, and vodka. This syrup will stop most colds and flu if regular dosing is begun as soon as symptoms appear and continued until symptoms dissipate. Wood also states that elder is useful for infants with dry, red cheeks and who have respiratory problems that cause the root of the nose to appear blue. It is a magical herb that stimulates dream-infused sleep. In addition, the flowers can be infused in oil and used to make an ointment or cream for chapped or irritated skin. The fresh flowers make delicious fritters and flavorings for cordials and wine. The berries, which should always be cooked before eating, make great jams, pies, and wine.

Can you tell that this is one of my favorite herbs?

Sambucus canadensis grows as a large bush reaching four to five feet high, produces white, fragrant flowers in early spring and beautiful racemes of deep purple berries in August. It is a short lived bush, usually living less than ten years. Elder manages most soils, requires reasonable moisture, and either sun or dappled shade. Do not confuse this plant with elders that produce red berries that are poisonous.

In pre-modern England, a variety of elder with edible purple berries called the "common elder," grew to tree height and was often grown next to the

Elderberry syrup

6 cups fresh elderberries (or dried ones soaked in water until plump)

1/3 cup honey

1/2 tsp. powdered ginger or 1 tsp. fresh

1/4 tsp. powdered cinnamon

1/2 cup water

1 T lime juice

2 cups vodka

Wash elderberries, mash or blend them. Put through a small colander or strainer. Mix with honey, ginger, cinnamon, and water in a sauce pan. Cover and simmer 35 minutes. Remove from heat. Add lime juice and vodka. Pour into bottles. Keep in refrigerator for one year or even longer.

At the first sign of a cold or flu, take 1 tablespoon several times each day to prevent an infection from developing.

privy to deter the flies.

Use the flowers, fresh or dried, as tisanes or make a tincture of fresh or dried flowers. Pick the berries when ripe, but before the birds eat all of them, to make syrup. A decoction of the bark is emetic and purgative.

Fenugreek *Trigonella foenum-graecum*
Annual

The seeds of fenugreek are a common ingredient in curry powder. They are also used in synthetic maple syrup, vanilla, caramel, and butterscotch flavors. The dried leaves are often ingredients in oriental sauces, stews, and soups. The yellow-brown seeds are aromatic when heated. In old Iraq, up to four thousand years ago, fenugreek was used in childbearing to induce labor and stimulate milk flow. It has a long tradition as a tonic herb in Chinese and Ayruvedic medicine. The leaves were used for birth control, in sitz baths, and for menstrual pain, and are reputed to be a soothing remedy for gastric irritation. In addition, both seeds and leaves tend to lower blood sugar levels. The sprouted seeds add taste and crunch to salads and stir-fries and are widely recognized for their value in kidney and liver disorders and male sexual dysfunction. Western medical research has shown that one of the constituents of fenugreek has potential in treating cervical and liver cancer and others are useful in oral contraception.

This herb has a very long history of use in the near east where it grows readily. Even in Europe, it has been known for some time. Dioscorides, a Greek physician and botanist born in the first century A.D who wrote *De Materia Medica,* reportedly called this herb *telis* and used it in a pessary for gynecological problems. The Latin name for this herb means "Greek hay" and it was often grown as a fodder crop.

Fenugreek is an erect, aromatic annual growing ten to twenty inches high. It has small yellow-white flowers. It likes sun and well drained, fertile soil.

Harvest the leaves during the growing season and the seeds late in autumn.

Fernleaf tansy

Tanacetum vulgare crispum
Perennial

Tansy does a great job of repelling ants. Place some near the entrance to your doors to prevent ants from coming in. The leaves and flowers produce dyes and in the past were used for flavorings. Native Americans once used the flowers to induce abortion and excess doses of this herb do indeed stimulate abortion as well as cause convulsions and venous congestion of the abdominal organs. The seeds and leaves expel roundworms and threadworms, especially when used as an enema. Topically, tansy is used for scabies, lice, and fleas. However, tansy contains thujone and camphor, both of which are toxic, so is used only with caution and definitely not during pregnancy. Tansy essential oil is highly toxic.

Fernleaf and other tansies are native to Europe. Fernleaf *(crispum)* is a landscaping variety of tansy used in gardens because it is not as invasive as other tansies. It adds interest to a garden and grows up to two feet high, is aromatic, and has clusters of yellow flowers. It prefers partial shade.

Gerard wrote about tansy's use as a wormer stating, "The feed of Tanfie is a fiungular and approued medicine againft Wormes, for in what fort foever it is taken, it killeth and driueth them forth." (The seed of tansy is a singular and approved medicine against worms, for in whatsoever sort it is taken, it kills and drives them forth.)

Leaves and flowers are harvested throughout the summer.

Feverfew

Tanacetum parthenium
Short lived perennial

Feverfew relaxes and dilates blood vessels, is a specific for migraine headaches, and improves circulation to the extremities. Feverfew also lowers fever and is anti-inflammatory with some use in arthritis and rheumatism or fibromyalgia. The fresh leaf should be used for these purposes. Occasionally, users get sores in the mouth from eating the leaves. Feverfew also stimulates the uterus and should not be used during pregnancy.

Feverfew is an attractive plant with small white daisy-like flowers with yellow centers. It is a short lived perennial, but will spread by self seeding. This plant has a pungent odor and grows about a foot high.

Gerard wrote, "It is a great remedie againft difeases of the matrix. It procurreth women's fickneff with fpeed; it bringeth forth the afterbirth and the dead child, whether it be drunke in a decoction or boiled in a bath and the woman fit over it; or the herbs fodden and applied to the priuie parts in manner of a pultis."

The leaf can be harvested throughout the growing season. Grown indoors, it is available throughout the year.

Foxglove, purple

Digitalis purpurea
Perennial

The source of digitalis for regulating the action of the heart, the leaf of *Digitalis*, is poisonous and should not be used without medical supervision.

This plant produces ornamental flower spikes. The word *digitalis* comes from the Latin for finger because the flowers fit easily over the tips of fingers. It prefers well drained mildly acidic soil and partial shade. The plant can develop root rot if too wet.

Prior to the discovery of its benefit to the heart in the eighteenth century, Gerard wrote of *Digitalis*, "Foxglove boiled in water or wine and drunken, doth cut and confume the thicke toughneffe of groffe and flimey flegme and naughtie humours; it openeth alfo the ftoppings of the liuer, fpleen, and of other inward parts." (Foxglove boiled in water or wine and drunk does cut and consume the thick toughness of gross and slimy phlegm and naughty humours; it opens also the stoppings of the liver, spleen, and of other inward parts.)

Harvest leaves before flowering. It is toxic unless in specific small doses.

Fo-ti (*he shou wu*)

Polygonum multiflorum
Tender perennial

This is the legendary oriental elixir of life. A tonic herb, the root improves production of blood cells and the oxygen-carrying capacity of the blood and stimulates the liver, reproductive organs, and kidneys. It helps clear toxins and can be effective for some bacterial infections. It is used for menstrual complaints and menopausal symptoms as well as for high blood pressure and cholesterol. The stems may alleviate insomnia and anxiety. *He shou wu* means "black haired mister," which refers to the plant's reputation for bringing back color to grey hair.

Fo-ti is a climber growing in moist, rich sandy soil in the sun. It does best when protected from the wind. It is perennial in southern areas, but not in zone four except when the winter is very mild. It blooms in August with panicles of tiny white flowers.

Harvest roots in the fall. The stem can be harvested throughout the growing season. Tincture the fresh root or stem or dry the root for decoction.

Garlic

Allium sativum

Perennial, but generally harvested annually

Garlic has antifungal and antiviral properties. It is expectorant, so is an excellent remedy for colds, flu, and coughs. It promotes sweating, reduces blood pressure, is mildly anticoagulant, and reduces cholesterol and blood sugar. Along with honey, it was found in the pyramid of King Tut. It is a cornucopia of vitamins, minerals, amino acids, and sulphur compounds. It is highly antioxidant and also repels garden insects and pests. To top it off, garlic tastes great in soups, on meats and breads, in potatoes, and in most pasta dishes. *No garden should be without this amazing herb.*

Soup starter or pot roast seasoning

1 cup dried chopped carrot
1 1/2 cups dried chopped onion
1 cup dried chopped green pepper
1 cup dried celery leaf or dried chopped celery
1 cup dried parsley
1/2 cup dried chopped chives
1/4 cup chopped, dried, & partially powdered mushrooms—morel or shitake
1/2 cup dried partially powdered tomatoes
1 T dried powdered garlic
2 T dried savory
2 tsp. sea salt

Mix well and package.

For soup starter: Combine with 6-8 cups water—or part vegetable, beef or chicken broth. Add meat and/ or vegetables and salt and pepper to your liking.

For pot roast seasoning: Rub 1/2 tsp. of mixture into meat on each side. Dredge meat with flour. Brown in a heavy pan in olive oil, butter, or your favorite oil. Remove to a cooking pot. Cover with 1/4 cup seasoning mix for a small-medium roast and 1/3-1/2 cup for a large roast. Add 2-3 cups water, vegetable broth or beef broth. If desired, add 1/2 cup red wine. Cover and heat at 300 degrees for 2-4 hours — or use a crock pot following directions.

59

Much of the benefit from garlic comes from a property of the pungent taste. If you remove that flavor, you lose much of the value. To benefit your health, you need to taste the garlic and your friends and family members must tolerate your garlic breath or body odor. With other herbs as well using just some of an herb's constituents, as is often the case when using pharmaceutical company herbal preparations, doesn't work as well.

Garlic cloves should be planted in the fall—October in Minnesota. If bulbs are saved for planting, save the largest ones because they produce the biggest bulbs the following year. Mulch heavily with four to six inches of straw. Leave the straw on in the spring. The garlic stalks will grow right through it. Harvest garlic when the bottom three leaves turn brown. Be careful to dig the bulbs when the soil is reasonably dry. If you leave the garlic in the ground too long, it will deteriorate some, especially if conditions are wet, and therefore will not last as long in storage.

There are two main varieties of garlic—the softneck *(sativum)* often called Italian garlic, and the hardneck *(ophioscorodon)*. The Italian is the most common type of garlic. It stores well and its soft stems can be braided. Ophio or hardneck garlic has a more robust flavor. It generally has fewer, but larger, cloves and usually doesn't store as well as softneck. Ophio garlic sends up a beautiful globe of tiny lavender flowers that become bulbils as harvest time nears. However, the plant generally produces larger bulbs if the stalk is cut back before flowering, just after the loop in the stem has appeared. Elephant garlic, by the way, is actually a leek, not a true garlic. It is milder than other garlic and has limited medicinal value.

Like most other things, there is some science and a lot of art in growing good garlic. Harvested too late, the skins deteriorate, which reduces storage potential. Some places in the garden seem more fertile, producing larger bulbs than others. Temperature and rainfall add their mark. Garlic likes early spring rains, but prefers drier conditions as harvest approaches.

Have you guessed that this is another of my favorite herbs?

When you cook with garlic, it is best to add at least some of the garlic at the end of cooking to preserve more of its medicinal value.

Harvest the bulb in mid-late summer. Let dry with good air circulation.

Hawkweed (mouse ear)

Hieracium pilosella
Perennial

The entire hawkweed plant has astringent, expectorant, antibiotic, anti-spasmodic, and diuretic qualities. In spite of being astringent, hawkweed also increases salivation. It is used for all afflictions of the lungs and for inflamed kidneys. In addition, used both internally and externally, it helps heal wounds and canker sores.

Hawkweed likes dry locations and at least some sun. It creeps along the ground like strawberries. It is a perennial European native with neat ground hugging rosettes of hairy leaves and lemon-yellow flowers reaching to twelve inches.

There are many varieties of hawkweed. Of *Hieracium pilosella major*, Gerard wrote, "The decoction or the diftilled water of the herbe, taken inwardly or outwardly, doth conduce much to the mundifying and healing of greene wounds; for fome boyle the herbe in wine and fo giue it to the wounded patient; also apply it outwardly." He also says, "Pena and Lobel affirme this to be commended againft whitlows (an infection of the fingertip), and in the difeafes of the lungs."

Harvest the aerial parts when in flower in May or June to make an infusion or tincture. It can be dried or used fresh, but fresh is preferable.

Hawthorn *Crateagus oxycantha/monogyna*
Deciduous tree

Traditionally valuable for its astringency, hawthorn was used to treat diarrhea and heavy menstrual bleeding as well as kidney and bladder problems. More recently, in the late nineteenth century, its action on the heart was recognized. Hawthorn is a tonic for the heart, improving coronary and peripheral circulation, regulating the heart rate, and helping to normalize blood pressure. It is probably the least toxic of any heart tonics. It is also diuretic and antioxidant. It is sometimes combined with *Gingko biloba* to improve memory.

Hawthorn grows as a tree, usually fifteen or more feet high and there are many varieties, all having similar characteristics. Cultivars do not come true from seed and are propagated by grafting. They prefer moist soil, tolerate alkalinity, and like sun or partial sun. The tree flowers in clusters prolifically in spring and produces berries in the fall.

Flowers and berries are harvested in season and both can be dried for infusions and tinctures or tinctures can be made from fresh flowers.

Hemp

Of course, much has been written about *cannabis*, or marijuana. It is included here because the subspecies *sativa* grows wild on the acres of Honey & Herbs, often still showing up in the garden after many years of cultivation. A few stalks of the herb are left to grow each year, as a novelty, for educational purposes, or as a remembrance of the sixties. The hemp growing at Honey & Herbs is likely left over seed from when hemp was an agricultural product in the area for rope production during the 1940's.

Cannabis has been grown in Asia and the Middle East since at least 4,000 B.C. It was used for its medicinal action as well as for its fibrous qualities. Today, its possession and use are illegal or subject to strict controls in most countries in the western world. The THC (tetrahydrocannobinal) is responsible for the psychotropic effects of *Cannabis* as well as its therapeutic effects in pain relief, ocular pressure reduction, and to reduce nausea. The subspecies *sativa* is considered "hemp" and lacks much of the psychoactive components of *indica*. *Cannabis sativa* grows up to five or six feet high and self seeds, with the seeds withstanding many winters before germinating.

Gerard called *Cannabis* the "Indian dreamer." He also said "it drieth up the feed (seed —sperm) if too much be eaten of it."

The whole plant of *sativa* is used for fiber production and the oil is used for culinary purposes. The flowering tops of *indica* are harvested for medicinal and psychotropic use, which is generally illegal, although medicinal use is slowly gaining acceptability.

Heartsease (wild pansy)

Heartsease was once a potent symbol of romance. Traditionally, it was used for dropsy, respiratory catarrh, and skin eruptions. The small flowers are edible. Heartsease is primarily used today as a detoxifying herb for skin conditions, for arthritis and other autoimmune diseases, and for acute bronchitis. It is a good cough expectorant with a high saponin content. This herb is the standard herbal remedy for capillary fragility in patients on steroid medication and it helps bones knit after fracture. In addition, as an immune system balancer, it is a gentle immune stimulant. Heartsease

infused oil is good for cradle
cap in babies and for eczema.

Heartsease is an annual or
short lived perennial. It grows
from a few inches to a foot
high with small pansy-like
flowers that often bloom into
November in Minnesota.
Viola tricolor self seeds, so
will often continue growing in
an area even if it does not
survive winter as a perennial.

Use the whole herb harvested
while flowering as an
infusion, make a tincture from
the fresh herb, or make
infused oil. The fresh flowers
can be added to salads or frozen in ice-cubes for drinks.

Horehound

Marrubium vulgare
Perennial

Horehound is a well known cough suppressant and many know it from their childhood as horehound candy. It is useful for persistent bronchitis, asthma, and whooping cough. It is antispasmotic, helping to relax the bronchi and relieve congestion. For whooping cough, it is best combined with ginger. Prolonged use may cause high blood pressure.

Horehound is a gently spreading, long lived perennial that grows as a short hedge about a foot high, with bumpy looking leaves and a flower stalk that produces white flowers along the stem. Purple flower spikes make this a nice garden border plant.

Gerard said, "The fyrup made of the greene leafes and fugar is a moft fingular remedie againft the cough and wheefing of the lungs." and, "Being drawn vp into the noftrills it cleanfesth the yellowneffe of the eyes and ftayeth the running and watering of them."

Leaves and aerial parts should be harvested just before or during flowering. They can be dried for tisanes and work well with other herbs, such as thyme, hyssop, and meadowsweet, for bronchial complaints. Horehound leaves are also tinctured or made into syrup.

Horsetail

Equestetum arvense
Semi-hardy perennial

Horsetail is prized for its use in prostatitis, incontinence, and other genito-urinary complaints. Horsetail is also antihemmorhagic. Wood describes its use for nervousness and indicates that it is useful, as well, in strengthening the connective tissue, bones, arteries, and other tissues and is especially useful for knee and other joint problems. Horsetail is anti-inflammatory and antiseptic. It particularly helps release the pus of deep wounds.

Horsetail is an ancient plant, present during the dinosaur age. It spreads by spores and may be difficult to eradicate once it gets established. It grows in damp conditions. Although it is not cultivated at Honey & Herbs, it is found in the roadside ditches. Silica is the primary constituent of horsetail that gives it not only most of its medicinal properties, but also its scouring properties, which earned it the name "scouring rush."

According to Treben, the Swiss Abbe and herbalist Kuenzle said that all people of a certain age on should drink a cup of horsetail tea every day and all pain caused by rheumatism, gout, and nerves would disappear and every person would have a healthy old age. Certainly, this overstated its value. Treben also said that old people who suddenly develop difficulty urinating or have drop-like urination should use horsetail as a hot steam. In addition, she recommended horsetail's use for edema around the heart and lungs or for kidney disorders and advised horsetail tincture for sweaty feet. She stated that many mental disorders are due to faulty kidneys and recommended horsetail, yarrow, and stinging nettle tea and horsetail sitz baths for depressions, delusion, and fits of rage.

It is the stems of horsetail, which look like skinny bamboo, that are used for medicinal purposes. They are harvested at any time during the growing season, best dried in the sun (unlike most herbs), and dried for decoctions, rather than tisanes, or used fresh or dried for tincture.

Hyssop

Hyssopus officinalis
Perennial

Hyssop opens up dried out tissue. It is a strong mint that pulls out many toxins. The Bible verse, "Purge me with hyssop and I shall be clean" may or may not refer to *Hyssopus officinalis,* but it is apt. Hyssop is a protection herb that is antibacterial for deep-seated heat or lingering congestion in the lungs, stomach, liver, intestines, and kidneys. It is said to be the last thing Jesus tasted. The essential oil is anti-inflammatory and is sometimes used in baths for relaxation, but should be used internally only with great caution because it can cause seizures. However, combined with wood betony (S*tachys*), it has actually been used to treat epilepsy. Tiny amounts of the oil are used for some liqueurs such as Chartreuse.

Hyssop makes a nice border, almost like a short hedge, one to one and one-half feet high. Although it spreads somewhat, it is not invasive. Throughout the summer, it displays a beautiful purple spike. The odor of hyssop is distinctive. Although it is said to be used in perfumery, it must be in tiny amounts since hyssop smells a bit like skunk spray. There are those people who love the smell, though; perhaps they are those who need the herb for their health.

Of hyssop, Gerard wrote, "The fame (hyssop) made with figges, water, honie and rue and drunketh helpeth the inflammation of the lungs, the old cough, and fhortneffe of breath and the obftruvctions or ftoppings of the breafft ." (...made with figs, water, honey and rue and drunk helps the inflammation of the lungs, the old cough and shortness of breath and the obstructions of the chest.)

Hyssop is best picked during early flowering to make a tincture or tisane of the aerial parts, fresh or dried.

Jacob's Ladder

Polemonium caeruleum
Perennial

A remedy for nervous complaints, headaches, and palpitations of the heart, Jacob's ladder was used for epilepsy in earlier times. It increases perspiration so helps to lower fever.

Jacob's ladder is a clump forming perennial growing one to two feet high. It is a showy garden plant with purple flowers and is used primarily as an ornamental, rather than medicinal, plant. It likes moist conditions in sun to partial shade and it's best to cut back the flower stems to the base after flowering.

The leaves and flowers are harvested for tisane or tincture. The roots are harvested in fall for tincture or decoction.

Joe Pye weed (gravelroot)

Eupatoreum purpureum
Perennial

This herb has a long history of use by Native Americans. It is a cleansing diuretic, useful for stimulating the passing of urinary stones as well as for cystitis and urethritis. It is helpful for prostatitis, painful menstruation, and for strengthening the uterus and strengthening contractions at the end of pregnancy. A man named Joe Pye became famous for treating typhus with this herb, and thus the name. On an emotional level, this herb is said to assist the ability to discern between truth and falsehood.

This is a nice flower garden plant growing a couple of feet high with pink to purple flowers in corymbs. Its relative, boneset, looks similar, but has white flowers. Joe Pye weed likes damp conditions.

Harvest the root in fall to make a decoction or tincture. It is best used in small doses for limited periods.

Lady's mantle

Alchemilla vulgaris/xanthochlora
Perennial

An astringent with salicilic compounds, lady's mantle relieves pain and helps rid tissue of excess fluid and control diarrhea. In addition, lady's mantle helps to control heavy menstruation and hemorrhage and to regulate periods. It is an important woundwort and is useful for ear and vaginal infections as well as for tissue tears. It helps strengthen the uterus to prevent miscarriage. Lady's mantle also helps lift abdominal tissue after childbirth.

Alchemilla means the "little magical one," and the herb was thought to have magical powers because of the way the leaves hold water or dew. The name of this herb derives from its association with the Virgin Mary. Maria Treben noted that lady's mantle is used, along with yarrow, to help bring on menstruation in pubertal girls when menstruation is delayed. She also stated that rinses with lady's mantle help healing after tooth removal.

The Swiss Abbe Kuenzle stated, "Through early and prolonged application of this medicinal herb two-thirds of all operations performed on women would be unnecessary, since it heals all inflammations of the abdomen, fever, burning suppuration, ulcers and hernia. Every woman in childbed should drink much of this tea. Some children would still have their mother, some stricken widower his wife, had they but known this herb." Kuenzle also recommended this herb for children who have weak muscles.

Lady's mantle may be difficult to grow, especially in alkaline soils. It likes slightly acidic and moist, but well drained soil in sun or partial shade. It grows close to the ground with leaves about three inches in diameter with seven to nine lobes in an open fan shape with small yellow flowers.

Aerial parts are harvested before or while flowering to make infusions or tinctures. The fresh herb is also infused in oil to make ointments for vaginal itchiness or irritation. Usually tinctures are used for female disorders, but infusions are better for diarrhea and edema.

Lavender

Lavendula officinalis
Perennial

This is an aromatic, uplifting herb. The essential oil is widely used for its scent, as in sachets, and in baths for nervous exhaustion and headaches. Lavender is also used internally for depression, irritability, and tension headaches and makes a pleasant tasting tea. It stimulates circulation and relieves spasms. Both flowers and leaves are edible and a nice jelly is made with the flowers. The oil is good for insect stings and minor burns.

Sunny conditions are necessary for lavender to flower well. The plant likes slightly alkaline and well drained soil. Most varieties do not manage cold Minnesota winters. However, Munstead and Hidcote varieties of *Lavendula officinalis* can usually survive the winter—with mulching that shouldn't be removed too early in the spring. The plant grows as a small shrub about one foot high, with greyish-green bushy small leaves and spikes of aromatic purple flowers.

Harvest the flowers near the end of flowering. Use fresh or dried for tea or tincture, although, as usual, the fresh is always best. Leaves and flowers are sometimes used in cooking. The essential

Peaches in lavender syrup

4 cups water
1/4 cup sugar
3/4 cup honey
2 rounded tsp. dried lavender buds
5 peaches, peeled, pitted, and sliced
Frozen vanilla yogurt or ice cream
Fresh lavender sprigs for garnish

Bring first 3 ingredients to boil in a heavy pan, stirring to dissolve sugar. Stir in lavender. Add peaches. Simmer 8 minutes. Remove peaches. Bring liquid to boil and cook about 10 minutes. Cool slightly. Put yogurt or ice cream on top. Pour syrup over and garnish with fresh lavender.

oil is one of the most pleasant aromatic oils available. Dried flowers make wonderful sachets and aromatic pillows.

Lemon balm

Melissa officinalis
Somewhat tender perennial

Lemon balm is a sweet, pungent herb with a wonderful lemony taste. Useful by itself, it is also a great addition to any other herbal tisanes, adding a lemon aroma and flavor. *Melissa* is good for tension and depression. It is a gentle relaxing herb, useful for good sleep as well as for digestive upsets that accompany anxiety. Wood says it is especially good for people with baby-like personalities who complain frequently. It is refreshing and cooling and good for feverish colds. Some have found it useful for children with ADHD (attention deficit hyperactivity disorder). Lemon balm also helps repel many insects and is anti-viral and antibiotic. *Melissa's* antiviral effects are especially good for cold sores; the essential oil (ideally) or an infused oil should be applied directly to the sore and a tisane or tincture taken internally as well. Although generally extremely safe, *Melissa* slightly inhibits thyroid production, so should be used cautiously for persons whose thyroid is not functioning well.

Lemon balm grows best in zones five through nine, requiring mulching if grown further north. However, since it self seeds, some plants should grow from season to season even if they don't make it as perennials. It likes full sun to partial shade and sandy, well-drained soil. Seeds can be planted directly in the soil in the spring and can withstand light frosts. The lemon balm plant reaches one to two feet high. Pick a leaf of *Melissa* on an early July morning, rub it between your fingers, and you'll smell the intense sweet sourness to the point that you can almost taste it. *Melissa* is a Greek word for the honey bee and the bees love to visit the tiny yellow inconspicuous flowers of lemon balm.

Collect the leaves of *Melissa* in mid to late summer and, if being dried for tea, dry them quickly. Use a fresh leaf in any tea you drink or make a wonderful tisane from fresh leaves. They are also a tasty addition to fruit salads. The lower leaves on the plants have the highest degree of essential oil.

If you plan to use lemon balm as a medicine, make a tincture from fresh leaves harvested before flowering. The leaves, fresh or dried, make a pleasant tasting tisane. The essential oil helps relieve depression and assists in relaxation.

Lemon grass

Cymbopogon citrates
Tender perennial

Native to southeast Asia, lemon grass is integral to Thai, Vietnamese, and Indian cooking. It gives a tang that neither fresh lemon nor other lemon herbs provide. Its fragrant essential oil is used in perfumery and aromatherapy. This cooling herb increases perspiration and relieves spasms. It also has antifungal and antibacterial actions. It is used for mild feverish illnesses. Externally it is used either as an oil or by applying the plant directly to the skin for scabies, lice, athlete's foot, and ringworm.

Lemon grass can only survive as an annual in Minnesota, so it doesn't produce magnificently wonderful giant stalks. However, even so, harvested late in the season, it provides a delectable enhancement for any southeast Asian dish. For cooking, cut the stalk off at ground level and remove the top greener part of the grass leaving about six inches. Peel the outer green casing to expose the lighter stalk. Mince very finely because this herb is very fibrous. Sprinkle in soups and on salads, chicken, and fish; add to Asian dishes or add as a zest to barbecue sauce.

Hot peanut sauce

2 stalks lemon grass
4-6 fresh chilies, depending upon hotness
1 large onion
2 tsp. fish sauce (omit if necessary)
3 cloves garlic
1 1/2 cups coconut milk
1 cup water
2 T lemon juice
1 T sugar
6 T olive oil
2 tsp. salt
4 T ground peanuts or peanut butter

Put lemon grass, chilies, onion, fish sauce, and garlic in blender. Blend. Heat oil for about 3 minutes. Add all other ingredients except peanuts and simmer a few minutes. Stir in peanuts. Cool.

The leaves and upper stalk—fresh or dried—make a great tisane and, as indicated above, the plant oil is used for fungal skin conditions. Lemongrass is also a wonderful addition to many herb blends. For cooking, use fresh, frozen, or dried.

Lemon verbena

Aloysia triplylla
Tender deciduous shrub

Native to Chile, lemon verbena has a wonderful lemon aroma and taste. Although seldom used medicinally, it helps relieve digestive spasms, reduces fever, and has a mild sedative effect. It is bactericidal so is good for mild illnesses. Whether used medically or not, it makes a wonderfully refreshing tisane and is a nice addition to other herbal "teas." The essential oil is used in aromatherapy for stress and to improve liver function. When walking through the garden, there is almost nothing better than picking a lemon verbena leaf, rubbing it, and inhaling the aroma. The leaves retain their aroma well, even when dried.

In colder zones, lemon verbena rarely survives winters, so is best grown as a container plant or as an annual. When it does survive a winter, it often looks dead in the spring until early summer when new shoots appear.

Harvest leaves throughout the growing season. Dry to use in tisanes or for flavoring drinks. Add fresh to salads and fresh or dried to salad dressings.

Licorice

Glycerrhiza glabra
Perennial

Licorice is a detoxifier that helps balance the immune system, so is especially useful in autoimmune disorders. The sweetness in it stimulates the production of hydrocortisone, aiding in arthritic-like conditions. Licorice is also anti-inflammatory and expectorant and assists in the healing of gastric ulceration. Excessive doses cause water retention and high blood pressure. It should be used only under the direction of a qualified practitioner for those with cardiac or circulatory issues.

Gerard sayeth, "…with the juice of the licorice, ginger and other fpices, there is made a certaine bread or cake, called Ginger-bread, which is very good againft the cough, and all infirmities of the lungs and breaft; which is caft into moulds, fome of one fafhion, fome of another."

Licorice is native to the Mediterranean region and Asia. It is a perennial and grows and over-winters in zone four, but doesn't thrive in northern climates. The variety *Pontefract* is the most hardy. Licorice does best in a semi-shady area.

Harvest the root in fall. Chew the root or make a decoction or tincture.

Lobelia, greater

Lobelia siphilitica
Perennial

Diaphoretic, emetic, and cathartic, greater lobelia has been used in dropsy, diarrhea, and syphilis. *Lobelia inflata,* a smaller annual plant that self seeds, is used mostly for respiratory complaints and is reputed to assist in the cessation of smoking tobacco.

Lobelia siphilitica grows twenty-four to twenty-six inches high and displays blue flower spikes. It likes light shade and prefers mildly acidic soil, so doesn't thrive in the more alkaline soil at Honey & Herbs. It likes water, attracts bees, and self seeds, but not prolifically. This herb is native to the eastern and central parts of the United States. When invaders spread venereal disease to this country, the Native Americans employed lobelia to treat it.

Greater lobelia is a perennial; however, it may not over-winter in zone four, so mulch well and good luck.

Use the root harvested in the fall for decoction or tincture. It should be used in small doses. Larger doses may cause vomiting.

Maidenhair tree

Gingko biloba
Deciduous tree

Gingko promotes circulation, especially to the brain, head, and extremities and has been widely used for preventing dementia or reducing its advance. It also treats irregularity of the heartbeat. Mildly anti-clotting, it should be used with caution for those concurrently taking anticoagulants, such as coumadin or herbs that contain anti-clotting constituents. *Gingko* has also been used for asthma, bronchial congestion, and allergic symptoms. The leaves help to heal leg ulcers and hemorrhoids. It has long been considered a sacred tree in China and Japan.

The Maidenhair tree is native to China, but it is hardy and will grow in the colder climates of the Upper Midwest. Described as a "botanical dinosaur" by Deni Bown, the maidenhair tree is basically unchanged from its ancestors growing two-hundred million years ago. It is an interesting tree that grows to about fifteen feet or higher and has distinctive large fan shaped leaves. To flower, both male and female trees are necessary, but it is generally better to have non-flowering trees because the smell of the fruit produced on female trees is unpleasant. *Gingko* likes sun and well drained soil. It should not be pruned because it will die back if pruned significantly.

Use the leaves, which are bitter and unpleasant tasting, for tincturing, or dry and grind to put in capsules. The nuts, growing only on fertilized female trees, can be roasted and used in alcoholic drinks, soups, and stir-fries. The nuts are also used in traditional Korean cooking.

Marshmallow   *Althea officinalis*
Perennial

The first marshmallow confections were made from the root of this plant, which is sweet and somewhat gelatinous. A tea made from the ground root is palliative for dry conditions of the mucus membranes. It is also antibacterial. Its use for stomach or duodenal ulcers, sore throats, colitis, diverticulitis, and urinary tract infections is well known. The root was a traditional teether for babies. The leaves, which are less medicinal than the root, but still useful, are good in quiches and dips in place of spinach. The roots, when soaked in oil and used as an ointment, reduce skin irritations, boils, and abscesses.

Theopratus, writing in ancient Greece, advised soaking the root in cordials for coughs.

Marshmallow is a native prairie plant that stands about five feet tall. It has small pinkish hollyhock-like flowers with large, downy leaves. This perennial grows best in boggy conditions, but also manages drier soil. It grows from seeds scattered in late fall or from root division in the spring. It survives well in zone four, but may do less well in areas further north and would likely need some winter protection.

The roots, which are soft, should be dug in the fall from two-year-old or older plants, sliced and then dried for later use as a tisane. The dried, sliced roots should be ground but not powdered for this tea that has a slightly gelatinous quality. The ground roots are also a healing and emollient ingredient in old-fashioned hand-made soaps. Do not tincture the roots because the medicinal mucilaginous quality will not be available.

Meadowsweet   *Filipendula ulmaria*
Perennial

Anti-inflammatory and soothing to digestion, meadowsweet is a sweetly aromatic plant that is diuretic and diaphoretic, promoting sweating. It is the first plant from which salicylic acid was isolated—in 1838. Its constituents are similar to acetosalicylic acid (aspirin), but don't damage the gastric mucosa because the salicylic acid in meadowsweet is buffered by soothing, healing compounds. The name for this herb was probably originally "meadwort." Meadowsweet was used to flavor mead (honey wine).

Meadowsweet grows easily in alkaline soil and likes a good deal of water in sun or partial shade.

Gerard said of meadowsweet, "The fmell thereof maketh the heart merrie and delighteth the fenfes."

Harvest the aerial parts while flowering for tincturing or fresh infusions. Dry for later use in tisanes or grind for use in capsules.

Milk thistle   *Carduus marianus* (aka *silybum marianus*)
Biennial or self-seeding annual

Milk thistle is a liver cell protector and regenerator. It protects the liver against toxins and helps it heal from damage, including damage from chemotherapy. It counteracts strong poisons, such as poisonous mushrooms. It is also reputed to be a good hangover cure.

Milk thistle is a hardy biennial in more southerly climes, but at Honey & Herbs grows as an annual and reaches three to four feet high. Like most thistles, it will reseed itself, but not prolifically so is not invasive. It is a beautiful garden plant with its large green leaves, veined in white, and striking purple flowers. It needs sun, but tolerates almost any soil type. Seeds can be sown in late spring directly in the soil about one-half inch deep—or they can be started in flats. It will also self seed to some extent, creating new plants in the general area in which it grew. The *marianus* in the name comes from the folklore that the milk of the Virgin Mary ran down its veins.

Writing in the seventeenth century, Nicholas Culpeper recommended the seeds of this plant in distilled water for jaundice and advocated cooking the young plant in spring to cleanse the blood. Matthew Wood relates being called by a hospital to treat a case of mushroom poisoning and saving the life of a woman who ate a death cap mushroom, which is usually fatal.

All parts of milk thistle are edible including the flower buds that can be eaten as mini-artichokes before the spikes form. The seeds, however, are the most medicinal. Due to the spines on the seed heads, these are not fun to harvest, but well worth the effort. Harvest soon after the seeds form, let fully ripen and dry, then place in a paper bag and hit it with a mallet. Separate seeds and chaff by putting them in a colander with small enough holes so the seeds don't fall through. On a windy day, joggling the colander will let most of the chaff either fall through or blow away. Seeds should be ground slightly and tinctured for the most medicinal action, although chewing the dry seeds is an option.

Seeds can be roasted to make an herbal coffee that acts as a liver tonic, although it seems like a lot of work for a coffee substitute and this tisane will be less medicinal than a tincture.

Milkvetch, Chinese

Astragalus membranaceous
Perennial

Milkvetch is an immune enhancing herb that tones the whole system; it is helpful for chronic fatigue and improves general vitality. It helps lower blood pressure and blood sugar and improves circulation. The Chinese say it boosts *chi*. Milkvetch has a beneficial effect on the spleen, liver, kidneys, and the endocrine system. It is reputedly helpful for persons on chemotherapy for cancer, lessening the therapy's negative effects. It has been an important herb in China for more than two thousand years.

Milkvetch is a reasonably hardy perennial reaching about three feet high with sprawling stems. In summer it produces small pale yellow flowers followed by seed pods. It is native to Northern China and grows best in sandy soil. It can be propagated by seed sown in fall or spring.

Harvest the roots of plants that are four or five years old to make a decoction or tincture. The roots are a good addition to chicken soup.

Milkweed

Asclepias syriaca
Perennial, difficult to eradicate

Milkweed is rarely used for medicinal purposes today since there are other herbs whose similar virtues are recognized as greater. The shoots of milkweed can be eaten, especially in early spring, but it is important to be sure to use milkweed, not dogbane, which is poisonous. Boil the plant in two changes of water to remove the toxicity of the sap. A root decoction strengthens the heart, relieving edema, and soothes the nerves. It also promotes sweating and is expectorant.

Although milkweed is an attractive plant, it is not the best plant to use for garden beauty because it readily self seeds and it is difficult to remove the roots from the garden. However, it is an important plant because the monarch butterfly larvae depend upon it exclusively for food.

Shoots are eaten after boiling. Roots are used in decoctions or tinctures.

Mint

Mentha piperita, spicata, etc.
Perennial

Peppermint, apple mint, spearmint, lavender mint, chocolate mint, English mint, and others assist digestion by helping to relax muscles of the digestive tract and by stimulating bile flow. The menthol in mints is antiseptic, decongestant, and analgesic and gives them the typical smell and taste. Mints also promote sweating in fevers. English mint is the best to use in cooking for pears, lamb, potatoes, and for mint jelly and mint juleps, while peppermint is the most beneficial for digestion.

Mints may irritate mucus

Mint syrup

1 ounce fresh peppermint or spearmint
1 and 1/2 cups sugar
1/2 cup honey
1 cup water.

Rinse the mint and drain. Put sugar and honey in small saucepan. Cut mint into small pieces and add to sugar & honey. Add water. Bring to simmer, stirring frequently until sugar is dissolved. When it starts to simmer rapidly, remove from heat and set aside to infuse for 20 minutes. Let Strain, discarding mint to compost. cool. Store in refrigerator for 2-3 weeks.

Use in summer drinks, alcoholic or non.

75

membranes, often interfere with homeopathic remedies especially if used regularly, and are not advised for infants.

Most mints spread by their roots and will invade much of the garden space around them, so it is best to plant them in pots or in gardens separate from other plants. All are aromatic and have square stems. Mints grow wild and have been heavily hybridized, so identification is often difficult.

Harvest the leaves before flowering for the best taste and most volatile oil. Dry for use as a tea. Mint can also be tinctured or, distilled, made into an essential oil.

Motherwort
Leonurus cardiaca
Invasive perennial

Motherwort, a bitter mint, is a tonic, especially for the heart, and is particularly useful for easing heart palpitations. It lowers blood pressure and reduces the risk of thrombosis, especially in women. The alkaloids ease uterine contractions, so are helpful during menstruation. This herb also relieves menopausal hot flashes, especially in women with nervous tension. It is antispasmotic, with some antibacterial and antifungal effects, and is one of the best nervines for women.

This plant is extremely invasive, so the flower stalks should be cut before seeding or the plant will spread and grow in any open ground in the area. It is like a thistle in appearance and produces pink-mauve flowers along the stem. The flowers become prickly burs as the season progresses.

Harvest the aerial parts at the very beginning of flowering. For use as a tisane, harvest motherwort before the spiky seed heads form along the flower stalks. Make a tisane or tincture from the fresh aerial parts, which also make a good flavoring for beer. Before the flowers and stems turn prickly, they are a tasty and healthy addition to soups.

Mugwort
Artemisia vulgaris
Invasive perennial

The aerial parts of mugwort are used in Chinese and Japanese medicine for moxibustion—burning the herb over the skin to draw out toxins—or internally for congealed blood and cold stiff joints. It is also recommended for hormonal irregularity (PMS and menopausal) and for uterine adhesions. Wood states that mugwort is especially helpful for women who have been through harshness, abuse, and abortions, and have stiff lower backs. Mugwort also helps expel parasites, especially tapeworm, threadworm, and roundworm, and promotes dreaming and problem solving. It was a traditional herb burned on the summer solstice as part of the solstice ceremony. Tiny doses are recommended for internal use and the herb should not be used constantly or for extended periods. Unless under the direction of a qualified practitioner, it should not be used internally by pregnant or lactating women.

Writing of mugwort, Gerard stated, "Pliny faith that the traueler or wayfaring man that hath the herbe tied about him feeleth no wearifomneffe at all; and that he who hath it about him can be hurt by no poyfonfome medicines nor by any wilde beaft, neither yet by the Sun it felfe; and also that it is drunke againft Opium. Many other fantafticall deuices inuented by poets are to be feene in the Works of the ancient Writers, tending to witchcraft and forcerie and the great difhonour of God; wherefore I do of purpofe omit them, as things vnworthie of my recording, or your reviewing." (Pliny says that the traveler or wayfaring man that has the herb tied about him feels no weariness at all; and that he who has it about him can be hurt by no poisonous medicines nor by any wild beast, neither yet by the sun, itself; and also that it is drunk against opium. Many other fantastic devices invented by poets are to be seen in the works of the ancient writers, tending to witchcraft and sorcery and the great dishonor of God; wherefore I purposefully omit them, as things unworthy of my recording or your reviewing.)

Mugwort grows about four feet high and extremely prolifically. Because it is so invasive, it should be separated from other plants. The flower stalks should be cut before seeding.

Use aerial parts for tisane, tincture, or as a moxa. It is quite a bitter herb, but is sometimes used in small amounts in the stuffing for game birds.

Mullein

Verbascum thapus
Self-seeding biennial

A relaxing expectorant for dry, hard coughs, mullein is especially good for children with asthma. It is healing for throat inflammation, is lubricating, antiseptic, analgesic, and curbs mucus production. Greek mythology claims that Ulysses took mullein on his travels to protect him from evil. Infused mullein oil makes a soothing remedy for earache as well as a remedy for boils and wounds. Mullein relieves urinary tract infections, arthritic pain, and chilblains.

Gerard described one of the virtues of mullein, "… boyled in water and drunke is good for them that are broken and hurt inwardly, and prevaileth much against the old cough." He also says, "The leaves worne vnder the feet day and night, in the manner of a shoe fole or fock, bringeth down in yong maidens their defired fickneffe, being kept under their feet with some focks or other thing for falling away." (The leaves worn under the feet day and night in the manner of a shoe sole or sock brings down in young maidens their desired sickness—menstruation—being kept under their feet with some socks or other thing from falling away.)

This biennial herb produces a whorl of large, soft leaves with flower spikes climbing three to five feet high with hundreds of tiny yellow flowers. The flowers, which are used in tisanes or tinctures, must be collected individually. Mullein is an attractive garden plant at the back of a garden. It self seeds, but not prolifically. Fields in farming country often display some mullein plants growing as "weeds."

Use the flowers for tincture or tea and infuse them in olive oil for earaches.

Onion

Allium cepa
Biennial

There are about seven hundred species of onions, which are universally used as vegetables, flavorings, and for medicine. Sulphur compounds create the odor of onions as well as much of the medicinal action in helping to protect against infection. Onion tea is a good remedy to reduce symptoms of the common cold. Onions also help reduce blood pressure and slightly diminish clotting time and blood sugar. They are expectorant and diuretic. Applied externally, raw onion diminishes boils and acne.

This plant is biennial, producing various sized bulbs. Most often, however, onions are planted from "sets" (small plants), and grown as annuals.

Use the bulbs in cooking or for a tisane, especially during the early stages of a viral infection.

Oregano *Origanum vulgare*
Perennial

*O*riganum vulgare is sometimes called wild marjoram, which is distinct from sweet marjorum, *Origanum majorana*. Commercially dried oregano is usually made from Greek or Turkish marjoram, *Origanum vulgare* subspecies *hirtum,* or Mexican oregano, which is not truly of the *origanum* species. In addition, oregano grown in southern climates is generally more flavorful than that grown in northern climates. Oregano is one of the few herbs whose pungency increases with drying. Used primarily for cooking, it is good with strong flavors such as chili, pizza, and Greek, Italian, and Mexican cooking. Some varieties are more full flavored than others. As a medicine, *Oreganum vulgare* helps relieve symptoms of coughs, colds, and mild feverish illnesses. Used externally as an oil, it helps relieve muscle and joint stiffness and aching as well as bronchial congestion. Oregano stimulates the uterus, so should not be used in medicinal amounts during pregnancy.

A hardy perennial, *Oreganum vulgare* likes sunny conditions in well drained alkaline soils. Some other types are not as hardy. Oregano gradually spreads in the garden and generally produces purple or pink flowers in panicles, with some varieties producing white flowers. Because there are so many varieties and hybrids, identification is often difficult.

Use the leaves for cooking and infuse both leaves and flowering tops for tea. Oil of oregano has been widely touted for its healing effects, but it is likely that at least some of these oils are not really from the *Oreganum* species, but from *Thymus capitatus*, called Spanish oregano.

Making herbal vinegars

First, harvest the herbs you wish to use for the vinegar. Wash and let air dry. (Water can turn vinegar cloudy.) When herbs are well dried, place in a sterilized quart jar and fill, gently pressing herbs into the jar. Add vinegar and fill to the top of the jar. Use either organic wine vinegar or your own that you make from vinegar mother. White wine vinegar works best for most herbs and creates the prettiest finished product. With strong herbs such as basil and rosemary, red wine vinegar is also a good choice, but the vinegar will be so dark you cannot see the herbs displayed in it.

After filling, cover and place in a dark place for about two weeks. Place a fresh sprig or two of the same kind of herbs you used for the vinegar infusion into the cleaned vinegar bottles, using mostly sprigs from small-leaved plants since they will display best. Strain the infused vinegar into the jars with the herbal "decoration." Discard the herbs that were used for the infusion. Cover and strain the finished vinegars. Seal with beeswax or other seals.

Lemon herb pepper vinegar

Lemon thyme, pineapple sage, tarragon, lemon verbena, savory, and peppercorns infused in white wine vinegar.

Great on fish, chicken, and in fruit salads.

Italian blend vinegar

Basil, rosemary, oregano, savory, and garlic in white or red wine vinegar

Wonderful in vinaigrettes, on red meats, and in pasta dishes

Red raspberry vinegar

Red raspberry leaves, lemon verbena, and red raspberries in white wine vinegar

This makes a flavorful vinaigrette for salads. Also sprinkle on fresh fruit for a zesty taste.

Nasturtium
Tropaeolum majus/minus
Annual

Nasturtium flowers are edible and high in vitamin C. They provide energy, condition the skin and hair, increase resistance to fungal and bacterial infections, and help clear excess mucus. The leaves of nasturtium have a peppery flavor and can serve as a pepper substitute. Medicinally, they are used for scurvy, genito-uninary infections, and respiratory infections as well as for skin eruptions and minor injuries.

Nasturtium is a nice garden flower with a variety of colors. *Tropaeolum majus* is a climber with vines reaching up to six feet, while *Tropaeolum minus* grows about twelve inches high and is ideal in borders, window boxes, and hanging baskets. This plant grows best in poor to moderate soils because very rich soils make it produce more leaves than flowers. It is beneficial to plant nasturtium near cucumbers because it deters cucumber beetles. Planting it near the base of apple trees may deter aphids from attacking the trees.

Harvest the leaves, flowers, and flower buds. Eat in salads, dry for tisanes, or use fresh or dried in tinctures. Use fresh flowers to make nasturtium vinegar.

Parsley   *Petroselium crispus*
Biennial, usually grown as an annual

Parsley is an excellent potassium sparing diuretic that accelerates the excretion of toxins. It burns excess fat and is antiseptic for the urinary tract, so helps prevent and treat infections. Parsley also helps contract the uterus after childbirth and, eaten fresh, freshens the breath. Parsley tea reputedly helps get rid of kidney stones. In addition, parsley strengthens the digestive system. It contains vitamins A and C as well as several minerals. The root is more medicinal than the leaves; make root tinctures by soaking the roots in alcohol such as white brandy or vodka. The leaves are useful for the above conditions, but are not as potent, although they have a higher concentration of the vitamins and minerals.

Parsley originated in the Eastern Mediterranean and has been known as a medicinal herb for more than two thousand years. It grows well from seed planted in a sunny well drained garden and lasts late into the fall,

Parsley pesto

2 cups loosely packed coarsely
 chopped flat-leaf parsley
1 cup coarsely chopped toasted walnuts
3/4 cup grated Asiago cheese (or
 Parmigiano)
1 cup thinly sliced leeks
Sea salt and pepper to taste
1/2 cup olive oil
2 tsp. fresh lemon juice

Put parsley, nuts, cheese, leeks, salt, and pepper into a Vitamix or food processor. Turn on machine and slowly pour in the olive oil. Process until a thick paste forms. Add lemon juice and 2-3 T water to thin slightly. Adjust seasonings, if desired.

81

withstanding early frosts. It is harvested from mid-summer until the frost finally kills it. It grows six inches to a foot high. The flat leaved (Italian) parsley is the most medicinal, but the curly type is better known. The curly type is used primarily as a garnish. Germination may be a little spotty with parsley, so it is best to over plant and thin as necessary. It is also helpful to soak the seeds in hot water before sowing. They need a few weeks to germinate, so should be planted early.

Cleansing tisane (tea)

Using dried herbs, blend the following, breaking the herbs into small pieces by blending for a few seconds in a Vitamix or using a pestle and mortar.

1 cup red clover flowers
1/4 cup alfalfa
1/2 cup chickweed leaves
1/4 cup lemon verbena
1/4 cup dried, ground apple fruit
2 tsp. stevia leaves (for sweetening)
1/4 cup flat leaf parsley leaves

The German mystic and herbalist Hildegard von Bingen recommended parsley wine to improve circulation and treat heart conditions. To make parsley wine, combine ten to twelve large sprigs of parsley with one quart of red or white wine and two tablespoons white wine vinegar. Boil for ten minutes. Add one cup of honey. Strain and pour into bottles. Drink a small amount three times each day.

Parsley leaves are good flavorings for sauces, butter, dressings, stuffings, salads, meatloaf, and almost any meat-based or vegetable dish. They are a main ingredient of tabbouleh, a Middle Eastern dish. For a tasty appetizer, spread parsley pesto on crackers or baguettes.

Pineapple sage

Salvia elegans
Tender perennial

Pineapple sage has a wonderful pineapple scent and taste. It is used for herbal teas and is especially good in iced ones. Pineapple sage also goes well in chicken dishes, jams and jellies, and is a good addition to herbal vinegars. There is no known medicinal value.

The plant grows in sunny locations, has red flowers, and is perennial but will not over-winter in zone four. It can, however, be grown indoors in good light. Pinch to keep it bushy.

Harvest the leaves on sunny days throughout the growing season before the flowers appear.

Lost by the River

On a sultry afternoon in mid-July, basset hound Tracker, along with his son, Tike, wandered into the cornfield adjacent to our land. Earlier that summer the pair had often followed their noses in pursuit of alluring animal scents. On those jaunts, they had stayed away too long for my comfort, so usually I no longer allowed them out together unsupervised. That July afternoon, however, was so hot that I assumed they wouldn't venture far.

Bred to scare up rabbits, bassets love to chase them, although they would have no idea what to do if they ever caught one. Shortly after five o'clock on that sultry afternoon, I heard Tracker barking his "I'm chasing a bunny" bark in the cornfield southeast of our place in the direction of a wooded area. Angry at myself for letting them go, I beat the drum that sometimes would bring them back with the promise of a good treat.

They didn't respond to the drum. I heard no more barking. As evening turned toward night, I kept drumming. I noticed the full moon in the darkening sky and a sense of foreboding shivered through me.

Shortly past eleven that night, Tike appeared at the doorstep, dirty and panting. I scolded him and asked him where Tracker was, but then I cuddled and petted him, so glad for his return. It wasn't unusual for Tracker to follow the quicker and more agile Tike by several minutes or more. I watched at the window.

Midnight came. One o'clock and two. Tracker didn't come home and my foreboding deepened, along with my imaginings of coyotes and other creatures of the full moon. We'd heard mention of a bear sighting near town. A bear attack was among my sleepless visions that night.

When light came, John and I headed into the cornfield to the wooded area south of us, swatting swarms of mosquitoes along the way. The first woods was relatively tame. The next was rugged with hundreds of downed limbs crisscrossing each other, along with jungle-like weed and grass growth. Following many rains, there was standing water and, at first, that encouraged me, suggesting that Tracker would not have died of heat prostration out there the previous afternoon.

We saw what we believed to be Tracker and Tike's paw prints near a line of trees. After searching the woods, however, we returned with a sense that Tracker was not there. We knew the wind had come from the southeast that full moon night and consoled ourselves with the idea that Tracker had caught the scent of a bitch in heat.

Our phone number was on his collar. We waited for the ring of the phone.

It never rang.

The next day we again headed into the woods, this time also winding our way through a third wooded area. Still no sign of Tracker. Intuition told us that he wasn't there. But where?

I created an ad for the Swift County Monitor-News and brought it into town, stopping along the way at all homes anywhere near us. I left flyers telling about our lost white basset hound with long brown ears.

We had phone calls and support from neighbors, from our mail carrier, and from visitors to my Honey & Herbs shop. No phone calls came with news about Tracker's whereabouts.

A week after Tracker disappeared, we went into the woods again, with hope waning.

"Speak, Tracker," John would call, but we heard no barks of recognition. We found no body. We looked for coyote tracks and found none, although we had heard the coyotes howling some nights. We saw raccoon tracks where the ground was soggy. A new theory of Tracker's demise occurred to us—being drowned by a raccoon in the over one-foot deep sloughs that had developed from the heavy rains. That night I dreamed of drowning.

Tracker, our biggest basset weighing about 65 pounds, was also the mellow one, the one who would turn his head in submission when threatened with a growl or a bark from Lady, our oldest basset and clearly the alpha female. He was submissive even to his own son. "What a sad irony that it's Tracker who likely met a violent death," I lamented to John.

When two weeks had passed, I ran an ad in the regional newspaper, the West Central Tribune. I received several phone calls, alerting me that the Humane Society had a basset there. I called. It wasn't Tracker. About the same time, a stray basset hound had been found on a farm several miles south of town. Deputy Sheriff Hindberg called me, thinking it might be Tracker, and we planned to meet at the farm. I grabbed Tike, almost threw him into the car, and headed south. All the way there I kept saying over and over, "Please be Tracker, please be Tracker," although the description hadn't sounded quite right. It turned out to be a basset hound mix of some kind, clearly not Tracker.

Whenever I left our house, I'd put dog food on the deck, but I didn't really expect it to be gone when I returned. When three weeks had passed, I stopped believing that Tracker was suffering in the wild somewhere. John took another venture into the woods, this time searching for a body. But it was also at this time that I began having dreams in my sleep that Tracker came home.

A month had passed. John and I were dinner guests near Belview at friends whose family members were visiting from England. We arrived home about midnight and I took the dogs outside while John checked the messages on our answering machine.

"Marsh, come here!" he yelled.

"Someone saw Tracker," he exclaimed excitedly and started to replay the message. *"This is Mike Grossman. My son and I were canoeing the Chippewa River this afternoon. We put in at the bridge about two miles from your place. Some half-mile down the river on a ledge below the main bank, we saw what I think is your dog. He looked pretty bad, but he's alive."* Mike said he'd put his canoe in again in the morning to try to find the dog.

I couldn't say anything for a few minutes, but "Oh, my God," repeated over and over. John found two flashlights and we headed down to the river, guessing where Grossman had said he'd seen the dog.

Winding our way through brush, we heard a voice saying, "There's an easier way through there." Following the voice, we came upon a group of people around a campfire. Mike Hoffman from Hancock, who had been fishing there, helped us search that night, leading us back on a trail he knew well. We called and whistled, told Tracker to "Speak," a command that a month earlier had brought him a treat. We heard no response.

Finally, we headed back.

We tried to sleep, but excitement and worry combined to prevent slumber. I hadn't prayed for years, but when I heard rain begin to fall, I prayed, "Dear Great Spirit, please keep Tracker safe until morning." The rain stopped within minutes.

At six o'clock I called Mike Grossman, apologizing for the early morning call. He said it would have been okay to call him at three o'clock or anytime. I was sure the dog he described was Tracker. He gave good directions about where he'd seen him.

John got his canoe. I helped him get in into the river and he headed downstream, while I went on land, searching along the bank. Ten to fifteen minutes later, I heard John hollering from somewhere south of me, but I couldn't tell what he was saying. I called out, "I'm coming, I'm coming" as I began tearing through the woods, stumbling, but staying upright.

When I reached a clearing, I saw John carrying Tracker up the bank.

That vision of an emaciated dog clutched to John's chest will remain clear forever.

I ran to them and John put Tracker down. I knelt and petted Tracker with my left hand, while my right hand retrieved a can of cat food I'd put in my pocket before we left. I jerked off the lid and Tracker attacked it. I feared he'd eat it all, including the can, in his ravenous hunger.

His eyes were bright, though he looked like skin stretched over skeleton. He was alert, but so weak he stumbled and fell occasionally as I led him down the trail. John carried him from time to time.

John said he had almost missed seeing Tracker. He'd just canoed past the spot where Tracker lay when he looked up and saw his eyes peering down toward him, with just the top of his head visible. It was unmistakably Tracker. John paddled against the current, with adrenaline surging, calling to him and to me. Near shore, he jumped out and managed to pull the canoe onto land.

John rushed to Tracker who was lying on a ledge some four feet above the river behind a little mound where brush and grasses hanging from the bank above provided some protection. This spot had a graded path down to the river. Water had clearly been the lure for Tracker to climb down the steep grade from the main bank. Once there, he'd apparently been too weak to climb back up.

When the full moon again came up the night after Tracker came home, he was asleep on the couch, curled up next to me. He occasionally stirred and looked up at me. His warm brown eyes starring into mine replaced my visions of coyote and raccoon attacks. He smelled like ammonia, having consumed his muscles for energy, so the other dogs stayed away at first, but the odor was like perfume to me. I wanted to cuddle and cuddle.

A couple of weeks later, Tracker had enough strength to jump up on the bed or into his favorite chair, although he was still a little too weak to enjoy Tike's antics in attempts to get him to play. He'll survive, hopefully into ripe old age, thanks to Mike Grossman and his alert eyes, but a fence around our property will limit this inaptly named dog's escapades to our five acres.

When I go into town now, I look out across the countryside and remember those times that I'd scanned the ditches and fields for a glimpse of a wagging white tail or some long brown ears.

Letter to littermates

Lady basset hound and Tracker were parents to four pups. John and I kept one puppy, Tike, who was part of the previous story. He would occasionally write to his littermates, with my assistance of course, and had previously written about Tracker's disappearance.

August 23, 1997

Dear littermates,

I've got really good news for you!

A couple of nights ago, our human folks came home late. Marcia gave us her usual greetings and pats and opened the door to let us outside just as John began checking the messages on their telephone answering machine. John started shouting and Marcia made us come back into the house just a minute after we went out. She walked around the house mumbling something about Tracker.

It had already been dark for hours, but they left the house again and drove away. When they came back a little later, their voices had a strange edge to them—like they were happy, but scared, too. They didn't pay much attention to us. They went to bed, but I heard them stirring every once in a while—and talking to each other, and I heard the name Tracker every so often and I started to think about Papa again.

Before it was light the next morning, Marcia and John got up and demanded that we go outside and then made us come back inside quick again. Just as dawn came, they left.

It was later that morning when they came back. John came into the house carrying a dog that smelled just awful. He put the dog down and I barked at him.

What was that terrible smell? Why would they bring home a dog that smelled that bad? The dog was really, really skinny and I went a little closer. Then I recognized him.

IT WAS PAPA! But, he was lots skinnier than I am and he couldn't even get up on the sofa by himself. I was excited, but kind of scared of him because he smelled so bad. He didn't play at all, but he gobbled up food faster than I've ever seen anybody eat.

A few days later, he told me his story.

I couldn't breathe when that creature with the circles around its eyes jumped on me in the water. But, finally it let me up and I saw you running away. I coughed and sputtered and got myself out of the water while that creature chased after you. I was so scared I didn't know which way to go, but I started running and ran as fast as I could. I don't know how far I ran until I was so out of breath I couldn't run anymore. I laid down to rest and must have fallen asleep. By the time I woke up it was getting light outside and I didn't know where I was.

I figured I better get on home and get some food, so I started winding my way back, sniffing along my trail. I was awfully hungry. Then I smelled bunny and took off after it, figuring it could make a pretty good breakfast. Boy, were there lots of good smells out there! One led to another to another. But I just got hungrier and tired and I never found any food. So, I turned around again and thought I was heading for home and some good food.

It was hot then and I decided to rest for awhile, so I found a shady spot under some bushes and went to sleep. When I woke up I started heading back along my track, but I couldn't remember which track I'd taken when. By then I was really hungry and I was scared because I didn't know the way home.

I figured the most important thing was to get some food so I could think straight, so I put my sniffer to the test. I'd been sniffing quite a while when I found a dried up dead bird and it tasted pretty good. I sure did want some of that good food we got every afternoon, though. I went back along one my trails, hoping it would lead home, but after awhile it got dark. I was still scared about that creature that kept me under water the night before, so I hated to go to sleep, but I was so tired. So, I curled up under some branches and hoped nothing would find me there.

Boy, are there a lot of sounds out there at night. I heard twigs breaking and I lay as still as I could. I heard some howling, kind of like when all of us sing, you know, but it was scary to hear that sound when I was out there all alone. One of those creatures with the circles around its eyes ran close to me and I turned my head away and hoped it wouldn't find me. It didn't even stop to sniff.

In the middle of the night it started to rain and I was getting all wet. I hate to be out in the rain! I looked for a better place to hide and got down under some bushes where I didn't get dripped on, but it was wet and slimy under me. The next day, I tried to follow my trail home again, but the rain had washed a lot of the smell away and I just got tired and hungry. I hardly had anything to eat all day. There were some greenish-brown things that would hop up out of the grass and I caught a few of them. They were kind of crunchy, but didn't make much of a meal.

I was so lonely for Marcia and John. I thought maybe they'd come and find me like they sometimes did when you and I took off for a little jaunt. I was lonely for you, too. And even for your mom, Lady.

I kept wandering around day after day, trying to find a familiar scent. I smelled lots of bunnies and I even tried to catch them to eat, but they were too fast for me and after a while I didn't even chase them anymore. At first there was lots of water out there to drink, but the ponds of water started drying up. I always kept my eye out for one of those creatures with the circles around its eyes when I did find some water, though.

Those jumping bugs became pretty tasty after awhile. There were some crawling bugs, too, that weren't so bad. I was hungry all of the time, though, and kept dreaming about that good food at home, but I'd wake up with an empty stomach. I was tired most of the time. Sometimes I was so tired that I even lay down and let the rain fall right on me. By then I didn't think much about getting home, just getting something to eat and drink. I kept dreaming about home though.

One day I got really thirsty so I pricked up my ears and put up my nose to sniff out some water. Soon I heard a splashing sound not too far away and thought I smelled water, so I headed toward it. I got to a cliff and looked over and there was a lot of water running down below. How could I get down there? I wondered. I walked along the cliff and found a spot where I figured I could make it down without falling into the water. My legs were pretty wobbly by then, but I got down the first hill to a place that was kind of nice—a grassy patch with a little ledge over it where the grass hung down from above. There was a little path down to the water and I went down and lapped and lapped up that cool, cool water. Then I came up to that grassy patch and crawled back under the ledge and had a good snooze.

It got dark. I was hungry, but I figured I'd wait until morning to go up the hill. When morning came, I got another drink of water, then started up that steep hill, thinking maybe I'd look for home again—or at least for some bugs. My legs kept falling out from under me and I almost fell down into the water. I went down and got another drink and took another rest and tried again. The same thing happened.

Now I was really scared, but I was so tired and hungry I hardly cared anymore. I found a few slimy crawling things to eat that day, but that was all. The only thing that kept me going was those dreams about the good food at home.

I don't know if it was two or three days or more that I stayed there, mostly just sleeping. Then one day I heard some human voices down below in the water. Could that be Marcia and John? I wondered. I pulled my head up and looked over the ledge. There was a man and a boy in a little boat. They looked at me and waved to me. Boy, how I wanted them to come and give me some food, but pretty soon they were out of sight and I went back to sleep.

Night came. I heard some voices. This time I heard my name. "Tracker, Tracker, speak Tracker." It sounded like John.

Then I heard Marcia, too.

Oh joy! Oh joy. They were close enough to smell me I was sure. I waited for them to come. I hoped they'd have some food. But after a little while they turned around and went the other way. I couldn't believe they would leave me there. All I could hope was that they'd come back again and I kept listening, but I got so tired I fell asleep again. Awhile later rain started falling. I was so cold now and I was shivering and, even under the little ledge, I got splattered on. I didn't know if I could make it until morning that might bring some sun and warmth.

When I woke up, it was light and I thought I'd heard something.

It was John's voice, again.

He was down there in the river. He was calling my name. I didn't have enough energy to stand up, but I leaned my head over the ledge. "Tracker, Tracker," John shouted. Oh, how I hoped he didn't go down the river like the guys in the boat the day before. He was floating past where I was. I tried to bark, but my voice didn't work very well.

Then he looked back toward me and I knew he saw me. "Tracker!" he yelled, "I'm coming Tracker."

And then he was paddling toward me screaming, "Marsh, I found Tracker!"

He was coming over to my side of the water. Oh joy, Oh joy, I thought, he's really coming now. It seemed to take a long time when I was waiting for him, but pretty soon there he was climbing up to me. He was screaming my name and I've never seen him so excited. I wanted to stand up and lick him and jump on him, but all I could do was sit there and look in his eyes. I was so happy.

John picked me up and he carried me up that bank that I couldn't climb and I wondered why he could just walk up it and I couldn't. He did slip a couple of times, though, and I hoped he wouldn't drop me.

Then I saw Marcia running toward us. John put me down and Marcia petted me and started crying and kept saying "Tracker, Tracker, Tracker." She put her hand in her pocket and brought out something. I recognized it. It was one of those cans of food she feeds the cats. I hoped she wasn't going to give it to a cat!

She opened up the can and I got a sniff of it and grabbed the can out of her hand. It was food. It was real food. It was better than any good food I've ever had.

After I gobbled that food I was able to stand up on my legs. Marcia put a leash on me and we started walking. Pretty soon John put me in the truck and we were riding and I hoped they knew the way home.

Yup! I started recognizing the smells. And then, oh joy, I could see our house. John picked me up and carried me in and I saw you, Tike, and Lady—and a puppy I didn't know. I couldn't figure out why you barked at me, Tike, but I didn't much care. All I wanted to do was eat.

If you remember, Marcia and John would only give me a little food at a time. Marcia took me up on the bed. I was still shivering. She covered me up and snuggled next to me and I finally got warm and every time a bell went off that day, Marcia or John brought me some more food.

Well, that's Papa's story. He doesn't smell as badly now and he's not quite as skinny. He still gobbles up any food I leave in my dish—and any food the new puppy Pickle leaves. He even dares to eat Mama's leftover food. He doesn't play with me yet, and he doesn't seem to remember how to run, but I bet he'll remember pretty soon.

Marcia and John are putting up that fence they talked about, so Papa and I might not be able to go for long trips anymore, but I sure am glad to have him home.

Love,

Your littermate Tike

The Living Dead

Years went by. Tracker lived several years after he returned home. Eventually, all three basset hounds got old and sick and died. We buried them in a pet cemetery on our land with their food bowls serving as their markers. Looking for new friends, we found Mazy, a long-haired mini-dachshund, or perhaps she found us. Some months later, we got her a companion and named him Snicklefritz. The two mini-dachshunds had a litter of pups and we kept an energetic male named Ernie.

When Mazy was just a pup, she joined me at a Farmers Market where I had a booth next to the Humane Society stand. Mazy and Millie, a tiny grey tabby kitten, fell in love—or at least in like—and we adopted Millie. She and Mazy became best friends, rolling and tumbling and even sleeping together on our bed.

When Snicklefritz came along, Millie took second place, but the three pets often slept together, whether on a chair or in the bed. They sometimes batted their paws at each other in play or Mazy and Snikle might take pretend nips at Millie, like they did with each other. Games of "chase" through the yard were common, with Millie dashing ahead of the dogs and climbing a tree or jumping on the fence. When Ernie got old enough to play, he became Millie's friend, too, but he had his parents as best friends, and apart from sleeping together, the favorite play among the four pets was "chase." If Millie didn't want to run, she'd stop and the dogs would stop. Sometimes one of the dogs would lick Millie's face, giving at least the appearance of offering a kiss.

On a warm September day, I had just returned from the grocery store and was carrying the bags toward the house when I heard the dogs barking their *chasing-a-bunny* bark. Unlike basset hounds, dachshunds tend to be good hunters and Mazy and Snikle had become adept. Even little Ernie had caught a squirrel. I didn't mind their catching rabbits so much, since the rabbit population often decimated my gardens. I didn't mind that they chased the deer out of the yard, keeping the deer from nibbling on young trees. I didn't like it when they killed a squirrel or a chipmunk or a garter snake. I scolded them for that and usually confined them to the house for awhile.

When their barking became agitated and intense, I dropped the bags on the lawn and ran toward the barking. Nearing the back woods, I heard a cat yowling and began to scream at the dogs to stop.

Arriving on the scene, I saw Millie in the thicket. I shooed the dogs away, actually kicking one in my agitated state.

Millie was hurt. As I bent to pick her up, I could tell that her hind quarters weren't working right. I gently took her in my arms and carried her to the house, yelling to John to keep the dogs outside.

Millie's hind quarters were paralyzed, I was sure. She was panting and clearly in distress. I cuddled her in my arms and sat in a rocker, trying to comfort her. As the minutes elapsed, I expected her to die. But she continued to pant, more intensely at times.

I asked John to see if someone was at the vet's office.

The vet came to the conclusion I had already reached. Millie would die and euthanasia would be the most humane approach. Her injury had likely caused an embolus that blocked an artery to her hind quarters. I held Millie as the injection was given, telling her over and over what a good cat she was, my tears dropping on her fur.

We buried Millie in our pet cemetery, her food bowl serving as marker.

At home, my eyes focused on anything but the dogs. I had learned to grapple with some of the deaths that I had seen in country life. There had been snakes that got into the blades of the lawn mower, bunnies, squirrels, toads and an occasional bird. There were also baby raccoons that died after I caught their mother in a live trap and took her away, knowing she would likely kill our dogs if I didn't remove her.

This death caused much deeper pain.

I went to my computer and began to write as I often do when I'm upset. I sent an e-mail to a friend who loves animals the same way I do, tearing some as I told her about the awful event. I ignored the dogs and didn't know if I could even begin to reconcile their deed.

My computer sits within feet of the pet door that allows the dogs and cats easy access into and out of the house. While writing, I caught a glimpse of a cat coming through the door.

For a moment, I thought I was insane or that my grief had turned into a hallucination. Or that Millie had somehow awakened in the grave and crawled out.

Millie had calmly walked through the pet door!

The grave wasn't disturbed. I wasn't crazy. The dogs had obviously injured a stray cat, a grey tabby that looked like Millie—or almost like Millie. I remembered thinking that Millie's eyes looked funny as I held her in my lap, but had thought that pain was causing the strange look.

I was sad that the dogs had killed a stray cat, but I couldn't really blame them for that. Their nature is to chase and grab animals that invade their space.

That night when we all went to bed, Millie curled up by her friends, the dogs.

Tina does a Tracker

Thunder boomed and lightening flashed in the early morning hours. At dawn, another storm was coming in when a neighbor stopped at the home of Geri and Bruce Lachmiller to tell them that a friend canoeing the river the previous day had likely seen their lost Norwegian elkhound. The dog was sighted in a dug out area along the river, perhaps a mile south of the bridge near Lachmiller's home. This was the same river, in the same area, where Tracker had been lost eight years before.

Three weeks earlier, Tina, a nine-year-old elkhound, and Buddy, a young rottweiler adopted from the local humane society, had taken off together. Buddy returned a day later. Tina didn't follow that day or the next or the next. After a couple of weeks, everyone kept telling Geri to give up hope—the dog had drowned in the river or the coyotes got her or other nightmarish events had happened—but she kept praying.

Geri and Bruce grabbed clothes and found boots, then headed out from behind their home along the west shore of the Chippewa River. Through the wet thicket and downed branches along the bank, they searched for Tina, calling her name.

Finally, drenched and tired, they turned around without sighting her.

Bruce had to leave for work, but Geri called in sick. Tina's terror of thunder and lightening had routinely brought her into the bathroom where she would tremble until the storm was over and Geri knew she was out there by the river in a storm. She called her neighbor, Ron Kent. Along with his wife, he was the fulcrum in an informal telephone tree that set in motion whenever an area dog was lost.

Ron called John and told him the story. Half an hour later, we met Geri at the bridge, along with our canoe. Ron was there as well. John hadn't used the canoe since he found Tracker, but although we both were concerned about the canoe's stability and John's current skill, he put the canoe in the river as the rain continued to fall.

Geri and I began the trek along the east bank of the river, working our way through thickets of buckthorn, over slippery downed branches, and over vines that often tripped us. This was Geri's second trudge that morning and she had a bum knee, "but something keeps me going," she said as she moved swiftly along the bank. My memory of finding Tracker's emaciated body and bright brown eyes along this same stretch of river easily drove me forward.

We knew John was ahead of us carried by the current, but along with looking for Tina, I kept watching and listening for any sign that John might be in trouble.

In the meantime, John had been calling for Tina as his canoe moved rapidly in the river swollen from all of the spring rains. About a mile and a half down the river, he had almost given up hope of finding her when he spotted a dog on a ledge just above the river at the bottom of a three to four foot cliff. Puffing and paddling hard, he turned the canoe around and made it to shore.

The dog watched him with her front quarters on a tree that had fallen at river's edge. John tied the canoe to the tree, got out and gingerly approached the dog he was sure was Tina. She'd been lost and scared and he was a complete stranger. At first she backed away, but John offered her a can of cat food he retrieved from his wet pocket. She ate. John put his hand out. She smelled, then licked. Struggling, he picked her up and maneuvered her up and over the top of the cliff.

While John fought to get himself up the muddy embankment, Tina started to move away. Reaching up and forward, he grabbed her hair, saying, "You are not going to get away now!" Holding on to her and fearful that they both might tumble down into the river, he managed to get to the top of the cliff.

He started calling to Geri and me. To keep Tina in tow, he took off his wet sweatshirt and used its arms as a leash.

When we heard John's voice, I yelled as I had when he found Tracker, "We're coming, we're coming," and said to Geri, "Either he's is in trouble or he's found Tina."

We were scrambling over branches in the knee-high grass when Geri saw John. The grass kept Tina in hiding. We began to run. I spotted Tina and screamed, "He's got her."

As we neared, John saw Geri's eyes fill with tears. She bent down, hugged her dog, and sobbed.

After I helped John re-launch his canoe, he headed down the river where Ron had promised to meet him at the boat landing at Ambush Park. Geri and I walked toward home with Tina. While the clouds grew dark, threatening yet another storm, Geri and I joked about our looks—our drenched hair, my cheap blue rain suit and muddy shoes, and Geri's torn poncho and soaking jeans. We marveled at the synchronicity of events that reunited each of us with our lost dog.

Tina was in pretty good shape for having been in the wild for three weeks. She was thinner, but having started the adventure with plenty of pounds, she was not emaciated. She managed the trek back, stopping to smell some good scents and to squat and defecate, a sign that her organs were functioning properly. While Tina reunited with Buddy, Geri went into the house to fry a couple of eggs for her homecoming dinner.

Another cloudburst began about that time. I jumped in our truck and headed to Ambush Park where Ron awaited John.

Fifteen minutes later, I saw John rounding the bend.

Plantain

Plantago major
Perennial

Greater plantain can be chewed raw for sores in the mouth and gingivitis. For insect stings, chew a leaf a little to open its juices and then apply it directly to the sting. This herb is also used for a variety of skin complaints, including skin ulcers and the irritating effect on the skin of some herbs with volatile oils. It helps pull out splinters and toxins. It is used for diarrhea, gastritis, and irritable bowel syndrome. In addition, plantain is good for respiratory infections, especially those with dry coughs, and helps stem internal hemorrhage. It also assists in quitting smoking and clearing the lungs after one has stopped smoking, and can even moderate the pain of shingles.

Gerard wrote, "The leaves are fingular good to make a water to wafh a fore throat or mouth or the priuy parts of a man or woman." (The leaves are singularly good to make a water to wash a sore throat or mouth or the private parts of a man or woman.)

Plantain is a very common lawn weed; it even grows in gravel and especially in places that are often trod upon. It hugs the ground, except for the flower stalk, and grows with large leaves in a whorl.

Use fresh leaves as a poultice, a tisane or a tincture, or dry them for the same utilities. Harvest anytime during the growing season.

Red clover

Trifolium pratense
Perennial

Red clover is an alterative that helps cleanse the system, removing waste products effectively and slowly restoring health. It is useful for skin complaints, such as psoriasis, especially when combined with yellow dock and burdock, and has been widely used for bronchial complaints, including whooping cough. It is also is an anti-cancer herb, especially for uterine, lymphatic, and ovarian cancer and is especially useful when there is just one cyst or gland that is swollen. The leaves have significant estrogenic properties, and help relieve menopausal symptoms. Red clover helps open plugged salivary glands, is a mild blood thinner, and an excellent source of isoflavones, which are antioxidant and mimic estrogen.

The roots of clover fix nitrogen, so it is an important cover crop as well as being grown for flower production. In Europe it has been used as a forage crop for cattle since at least the middle ages. It grows well in the sun from seeds sown in spring. First blooming in June, it will bloom again if mown. It is a short lived perennial, but when well established self seeds. Red clover is readily identifiable not only by the flower, but by the leaves that have a grey-green V stripe.

Harvest the flowers along with the topmost leaves at full bloom for tisanes, tinctures, and ointments. For skin conditions, use red clover both internally and externally. Red clover makes a nice, sweet, yet slightly grassy tasting, tea. To be most useful, it should be taken daily for six weeks. The flowering tops add taste and color to salads.

Red raspberry

Rubus idaeus
Short lived shrub

Red raspberry leaves are a tonic to the uterus in preparation for childbirth, preventing early delivery, preparing the body for delivery, and hastening recovery. The leaves contain vitamins A, B, C, and K. They are mildly astringent, so are useful for diarrhea. Red raspberry leaf is a tonic for the prostate gland, as well, and makes a good gargle for sores in the mouth and sore throats. Of course, as a food, red raspberries are wonderfully sweet summer treats eaten fresh by themselves, with cream, or as a topping for other desserts.

Red raspberry is a perennial that produces stalks three to four feet high and is a bramble, spreading by producing shoots. Some varieties are June-bearing, others are ever-bearing. Although *Rubus idaeus* is of European origin, there were similar Native American species and it is the North American Indians who promoted this herb's use in childbearing.

Harvest the leaves before the fruit ripens and dry for tisanes. For childbearing, use the tea during the last trimester.

Rosemary

Rosemarinus officinalis
Perennial shrub, but annual in cooler climates

Rosemary is a favorite for culinary and medicinal use. It is especially valuable for strengthening the heart, therefore limiting or preventing cardiac hypertrophy and eventual heart failure. In addition, rosemary, like most culinary herbs, is antimicrobial—especially antifungal and antibacterial. It helps eliminate the bacteria that cause tooth decay. Rosemary helps digest fats and oils, so is useful in pasta dishes that may include cream, cheese, or oils. It is one of the major herbs used in Italian dishes and makes a

Italian salad

1 cup extra virgin olive oil
1/2 cup red wine vinegar
1 large clove garlic, minced
2 tsp. fresh basil, chopped, or 3/4 tsp. dried
2 tsp. fresh rosemary, chopped, or 3/4 tsp. dried
2 tsp. fresh savory, chopped, or 3/4 tsp. dried
1/2 tsp. sea salt
1/4 tsp. ground black pepper
1 lg. head romaine lettuce—or your favorite lettuce
1 1/2 cups sliced cucumber
1 1/2 cups crumbled Feta cheese
1 cup pitted, sliced green olives
1/2 cup Kalamato or Greek olives
3/4 cup roasted or sautéed bell peppers, ideally red
3/4 cup thinly sliced sweet onion.

Blend together the olive oil, vinegar, herbs, salt, and pepper. Blend until thickened. Combine the rest of the ingredients in a large bowl. Add the dressing and toss well.

great flavoring for poultry and
pork as well. It is especially good
mixed with olive oil and spread
under the skin when roasting a
chicken—or put a sprig on a
chicken breast when sautéing it.
In history, rosemary is associated
with memory and fidelity. It is a
mild pain killer and sedative, so
helps relieve headaches and
anxiety induced indigestion.

Rosemary is a very aromatic
perennial shrub in southern areas,
but grows only as an annual in
zone four. It will not grow from
seed, at least not during a season,
so small plants should be put out
in spring. Rosemary can be
propagated from cuttings from healthy plants. Small plants are often for
sale in the spring at nurseries or garden stores. Alternatively, order plants
or plug trays from such herbal vendors as Richter's Herbs or Nichols
Garden Nursery. Rosemary needs full sun and likes dry conditions.

Harvest the leaves throughout the growing season for tea, tincture, or
cooking. Rosemary dries easily either by hanging exposed to the air or in a
dehydrator at 105 degrees.

Rue

Ruta graveolens
Small shrub

As a homeopathic preparation, rue is used for sprains, strains, blows, and
contusions. As an herb, use only small doses for short periods. Wood states
that *Ruta* is suited to persons who strain hard to suppress unpleasant
emotions and have great tension in the cardiovascular system. It is an old
cancer remedy, helps strengthen fragile capillaries, and also reduces blood
pressure. In ancient Alexandria, it was considered an antidote to poison,
but rue itself is poisonous in large doses. Rue was used against the great
plague of the middle ages and continues to be used by qualified
practitioners for sprains and strains and ganglions of the wrist as well as
life threatening deep-seated infections. It also has traditional uses as a
protective herb.

Rue is an interesting garden addition. It is a small semi-evergreen shrub with grey-green leaves. It has been called "herb of grace" which refers to the tradition of using a sprig of rue to sprinkle holy water during mass. It grows best in well drained neutral to alkaline soil. It is best to prune it back each spring.

Harvest the leaves in spring or fall. Use very small doses in tisanes or tinctures.

Sage

Salvia officinalis
Short lived perennial

Garden sage is even more important as a medicinal herb than for its culinary value. Herbalist John Gerard, writing in the seventeenth century, said, "Sage is fingular good for the head and braine, it quickneth the fenses and memory, ftrengthneth the finewes, reftoreth health to thofe that haue the palfie, takes away fhakey trembling of the members; and being pvt vp the noftrils, it draweth thin flegme out of the head." The Chinese are said to have preferred sage tea to their own (*Camellia sinensis*) and given thrice the quantity of their choicest teas in exchange. Since antiquity, sage has been reputed to produce a long life. A thirteenth century verse says, "Why should a man die, whilst Sage grows in his garden?" The old herbals extol the many virtues of sage for curing or preventing most ills from disorders of the spinal column to dispelling phlegm.

Traditional use of sage for medicine in this country was for sores in the mouth and for sore throats. Sage tea was also used for fevers and for nervous or brain diseases. It was used then and now for menopausal hot flashes as well as for colds, painful joints, tension headaches, and palsy or Parkinson's disease. The volatile oils of this herb are strongly antiseptic, anti-inflammatory and anti-microbial. Some evidence suggests that an enzyme in sage may protect against Alzheimer's and other dementias. In aromatherapy, the essential oil helps remove excess mucus from the respiratory system in addition to improving memory and intuition.

Sage and onion, traditionally used in poultry stuffing, aid the digestion of fats and oils, so are especially useful in pork, geese, duck, and sausage, but of course are great with turkey as well.

There are many varieties of garden sage, some with white flowers, others with purple or pink ones. Seeds may be sown in the spring, but it is advantageous to buy small plants or use cuttings or divisions taken in the spring or fall. Sage likes well drained sunny locations and is perennial, but usually dies out after a few years. Mulch sage for the winter and prune back in the spring.

Chicken with leeks and sage

1 large roasting chicken
1/4 cup balsamic vinegar
1 T olive oil
2 T chopped fresh sage, plus two sprigs
2 tsp. chopped fresh rosemary
1 large or two medium cloves garlic
5 leeks, sliced (or substitute onions)
1/3 cup chicken or vegetable broth
1/3 cup dry white wine

Preheat oven to 400 degrees. Place chicken, vinegar, oil, chopped herbs, and garlic in large bowl. Coat chicken with mixture.

Arrange leeks and sage sprigs in roasting pan. Put chicken on top. Pour any remaining vinegar-oil mixture on chicken. Add broth and wine. Roast chicken until juice runs clear, usually 1 1/2 hours to 2 1/2 hours.

Snip fresh leaves as desired throughout the season. When harvesting for medicinal use, gather in full sun to best preserve the volatile oils (which is true for all aromatic herbs with volatile oils.) Usually you'll still be able to take some fresh leaves at Thanksgiving in Minnesota. They'll taste good, but will not look as appealing as earlier in the season. Sage dries well when hung to dry, but using a dehydrator at about 100 degrees better preserves the oil and color.

Use the leaves for tisanes or tinctures or use in cooking.

St. John's wort

Hypericum perforatum
Perennial

St. John's wort is an analgesic for nerve pain, especially for sharp shooting pain along the nerve root and for facial nerve pain (trigeminal neuralgia). It is anti-inflammatory and a tonic to the solar plexus, giving strength to do what must be done. It also helps rebuild and tone the liver. Although touted as an antidepressant, it is best used only for mild depressions or funks.

Treben recommended using St. John's wort infused oil for babies with abdominal pain or colic. Gerard mentioned the use of St. John's wort for deep wounds, referencing the blood red oil it makes. He also wrote, "Dioscorides faith that the feed (seed) drunke for the fpace of fourty dayes together cureth the sciatica and all aches that happen in the hips."

St. John's wort grows well from seed and will moderately self seed. Because it causes sun toxicity in cattle, one should be careful not to let it seed itself in pastures or grow wild. The plant with tiny leaves grows two to three feet tall, producing small yellow star-like flowers with tiny pinprick holes.

Harvest individual flowers for tisane or tincture, which turns bright red. Soaking the yellow flowers in olive oil creates a beautiful red oil, which works well for massage when nerve pain is involved, and can be made into an ointment.

Schisandra (wu wei zi)

Schisandra chinesis
Deciduous shrub

Sometimes called "Chinese Prozak," schisandra is astringent, sedative, and aphrodisiac. It is generally used for insomnia and anxiety. It acts as a tonic on all organs, but especially the kidneys, reproductive organs, and nervous system. In addition, it is good for allergic skin conditions and may increase fluid retention in the skin, which helps maintain a youthful appearance.

Native to China, schisandra is a viney climber that is attractive on a trellis. It grows in sun or partial shade. Both male and female plants must be grown to produce the berries, which appear in fall. The berries have all five flavors—sweet, sour, acrid, bitter, and salty, which is the meaning of *wu wei zi*. Traditionally, fresh berries were chewed for one hundred days. To survive in zone four, *Schisandra chinensis* must be mulched and even then a very cold winter can kill it off.

Gather the fruit about the same time you would pick Haralson apples, after the first light frost. Dry the berries, then use for tincture or decoction, or eat them fresh.

Sea lavender (stasis)

Limonium latifolium
Perennial

Sea lavender, often called stasis, is seldom used medicinally, but it is an astringent that is useful as a tonic, especially following a bout with diarrhea. As a gargle, it soothes lesions in the mouth and, as an ointment, helps heal other sores and ulcers. Gerard advised use of the astringent seed for dysentery and the "ouermuch flowing of womens termes and all other fluxes of bloud."

Stasis grows two to three feet high with a whorl of large leaves. It produces long spikes that have tiny white-purple flowers. Cut the stems and dry to use in wild flower arrangements.

For medicinal use, harvest the root in the fall for decoction, tincture or, infused in oil, to make an ointment. Collect the seed for tincture or powdering.

Self heal
Prunella vulgaris
Perennial

Use fresh aerial parts before flowering to stop bleeding and help wounds to close. As a gargle, self heal is good for sore throats, bleeding gums, and mouth irritations. As an astringent, it is beneficial for excess menses and other hemorrhage as well as for hemorrhoids. It also helps heal cuts, bruises, and minor burns. In Chinese medicine, the flower spikes are used to clear "liver fire" associated with irritability and anger, high blood pressure, headaches, and hyperactivity in children. Self heal also helps pull out heavy metals and is useful in treating and preventing cancer. Bown states it helps lower blood pressure and has antibiotic effects against some of the organisms that cause enteritis and urinary tract infections. Culpeper stated that this herb is called self-heal because when you are hurt, you can heal yourself.

A short creeping perennial with small leaves, which grows only a few inches high, *prunella* produces a purple flower spike. In some soils it can be invasive, but it hasn't spread significantly in the Honey & Herbs garden.

Harvest the aerial parts before and during flowering for infusion, ointments, and tinctures. Harvest the flower spikes in autumn and use dried in infusions for "liver fire" issues. The leaves are edible for salads.

Sheep sorrel
Rumex acetosella
Self-seeding perennial

Traditionally used for fevers, inflammations, diarrhea, excessive menstruation, and cancer, sheep sorrel is one of the ingredients in Essiac Tea, along with burdock, Turkey rhubarb, and slippery elm inner bark. This tea, brewed correctly, is a reputed remedy for a variety of cancers. Sheep sorrel has a high oxalic acid content, which is antiseptic and is especially good for intense fever. It's a good idea to eat one leaf a day during the growing season to prevent cancer—and it's tasty and uplifting as well.

Sheep sorrel is a short perennial with long lance-like leaves, which are sour. It produces rust colored seeds along its stem and readily self seeds. It is moderately invasive, but usually limits itself to the general vicinity in which it grew. The leaves are delicious in salads, bringing a sharp tangy taste, and are a tasty addition to sauces, soups, and soft cheeses.

Harvest the leaves and seeds for tisane or tincture.

Skullcap

Scutellaria lateriflora
Perennial

As with most plants that have purple flowers, skullcap is a calming, anti-spasmotic herb good for the nervous system—for tension, irritability, and sleeplessness. It has been used to treat rabies, epilepsy, schizophrenia, and to assist in the withdrawal from alcohol. Skullcap's name comes from the fact that the flowers resemble the skull cap worn by the Roman soldiers. It is not recommended for use during pregnancy.

Skullcap is a perennial that will spread somewhat beyond the borders where it was planted. It grows one to one and one-half feet high, does well in sandy, mildly alkaline soil in sun or dappled shade, and produces very small purple flower spikes.

Use the aerial parts collected in late summer for tinctures or tisanes. Tinctures are best made with the fresh herb and it is usually dried for tisanes. Small to moderate doses of this herb should be used because excessive dosage may cause giddyness, confusion, and twitching.

Solomon seal

Polygonatum multiflorum
Perennial

Solomon seal is useful for any musculoskeletal disorder, especially for problems with connective tissue such as ligaments and tendons. According to Wood, it tends to loosen tight ligaments/tendons and tighten loose ones. It is nutritive for weak people and healing for vaginal yeast infections. It increases psychic ability, according to Wood, and I have found it useful for persons whose early lives were harsh and who tend to be stiff. Solomon seal is a member of the lily family. Its shoots can be eaten before the leaves unfurl. The berries should not be eaten.

Solomon seal is an attractive garden plant, especially for the back of a garden. It grows four to five feet high, producing flowers along the stem, which later become purple berries. It spreads gradually over years and birds, who eat the seeds, may spread it elsewhere. It grows in well drained, but moist soil and does best in partial shade.

The roots have a wonderfully nutty flavor and are stunningly white, resembling bone. Harvest them in early fall for use fresh in tinctures or dried in decoctions.

Stinging nettle

Urtica dioeca/urens
Perennial

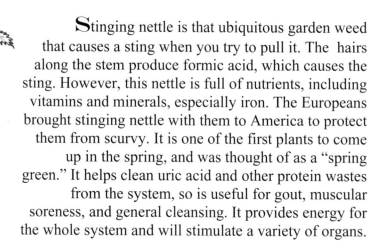

Stinging nettle is that ubiquitous garden weed that causes a sting when you try to pull it. The hairs along the stem produce formic acid, which causes the sting. However, this nettle is full of nutrients, including vitamins and minerals, especially iron. The Europeans brought stinging nettle with them to America to protect them from scurvy. It is one of the first plants to come up in the spring, and was thought of as a "spring green." It helps clean uric acid and other protein wastes from the system, so is useful for gout, muscular soreness, and general cleansing. It provides energy for the whole system and will stimulate a variety of organs.

Nettles is even helpful in restoring function to paralyzed limbs and, when used as a switch, it supposedly restores function to a non-functioning male organ! It can be eaten as a food, similar to spinach. For general good health, it is a good practice to drink nettle tea daily when the plant is harvestable in spring. According to Maria Treben, stinging nettle baths have cured sciatic pain and malignant growths and diminished coronary artery constriction, fungus under the nails, and eczema as well as a variety of other ills.

Gerard wrote of nettles, "Being eaten, as Diocorides faith, boyled with Perywinkles, it maketh the body foluble, doing it by a kinde of cleanfing qualitie: it alfo prouoketh vrine and expelleth ftones out of the kidneys."

Stinging nettle grows to about four feet high in most open places or at the edge of yards.

Harvest the leaves and stems in early spring when the plant is only four to eight inches high. Use in cooking as a spinach substitute. It retains its action best when tinctured fresh or used fresh, not dried, for a tisane. Freezing it is also a good way to retain medicinal value. Stinging nettle "tea" also serves as an organic pest control. Roots are medicinal, as well, and are best harvested in early spring or fall for tincture. Ointments for eczema, gout, neuralgia, burns, and insect bites are made by infusing the leaves in olive or safflower oil.

Stinging nettle artichoke dip

2 14 oz. cans artichoke hearts (can use marinated if you prefer more flavor)
8 oz. cream cheese, softened
1 cup fresh, packed, or frozen young stinging nettle leaves (picked when 4-8 inches high)
1 cup shredded mozzarella or Asiago cheese
1 cup shredded cheddar cheese
1/2 cup diced onion
1/2 cup mayonnaise
1/2 cup Dijon mustard
1 tsp. salt

Diced tomatoes and shredded Asigo or Parmesan cheese

Heat oven to 350 degrees. Drain and chop artichokes. Combine artichokes, cream cheese, stinging nettle, cheeses, onion, mayo, mustard and salt. Put in baking dish. Bake 50-60 minutes, until bubbly. Top with tomatoes and shredded cheese. Bake 8-10 more minutes until lightly browned on top.

Sweet cicely

Myrrhis oderata
Perennial

Used by Native Americans for diabetes, perhaps because the roots have a sweet taste but do not increase blood sugar, sweet cicely also treats anemia, coughs, and digestive disorders. The roots are antiseptic. As a food, the leaves are tasty and nutritive in salads, soups, and stews, add sweetness to wine, and mellow the sourness in rhubarb desserts. Roots are good cooked as a vegetable or, having been cooked and cooled, used as a salad with oil and vinegar.

Gerard recommended that the roots of sweet cicely, which he called *sweet cheruill,* be boiled, then combined with oil and vinegar, for "old people that are dull and without courage; it rejoyceth and comforteth the heart and increafeth their luft and ftrength (lust and strength)."

Sweet cicily has sweet anise scented foliage that does well in moist soil in semi-shade. It has a fern-like appearance and grows two to three feet high, producing small white flowers in umbels. It self seeds to some extent, but is not invasive.

Harvest the leaves, roots, and seeds for use in tisanes, decoctions, or tinctures. Leaves and the roots, which are the most medicinal, are used in cooking for soups, stews, and salads. The leaves are sometimes used as a sugar substitute.

Sweet woodruff
Galium oderata
Perennial

Sweet woodruff improves liver function and strengthens the capillaries. It also has sedative, anti-inflammatory, anti-clotting, and diuretic effects. The leaves are insecticidal, and although not very aromatic in the garden, increase in aroma when dried or put in acidic liquids. Traditionally, they are added to wine and fruit cups.

A creeping, low growing plant with whorls of bright green narrow leaves, sweet woodruff will spread to nearby garden space over time. It works well in beds with hosta and other shade loving plants, especially in alkaline soil. The leaves remain bright green throughout the fall and even retain color after a light snow.

Aerial parts, collected during flowering, are used for tincture or tisane.

Tarragon
Artemisia dracunculus sativa
Perennial

Primarily a culinary herb, tarragon is excellent with chicken dishes as well as with salmon and other fish. It has an anise or licorice-like flavor. Famous sauces such as Béarnaise and hollandaise contain this herb. Tarragon does well preserved in vinegar for use in the above mentioned dishes. While tarragon was called a "dragon herb" because of its use for venomous stings and snake bites, it is generally not used medicinally today, although it does stimulate digestion and, as with all artemisias, helps expel intestinal worms.

Dark green shiny leaves grow on this shrubby plant, which reaches about three feet high. It is best used in the spring and very early summer. The taste diminishes and the size of leaves becomes smaller as the season progresses. Tarragon requires light, well drained soil in a sunny location, and is very hardy.

Harvest the leaves for cooking. To dry them, use early spring harvested tarragon, which will preserve the oil and flavor better than that harvested later. To dry, remove the leaves from the stem, place on dehydrator trays, and dry at 100 degrees. Even so, drying is not as effective at retaining flavor as freezing or preserving in vinegar. Leave the leaves on the stem for freezing or making tarragon vinegar.

Chicken with tarragon cream sauce

Preheat oven to 350 degrees. Cut up one large chicken. Coat chicken pieces with flour. Brush chicken with olive oil. Sprinkle with a little fresh or dried tarragon. Bake until the chicken juices run clear, about 45-60 minutes.

For tarragon cream sauce:

2 T flour
2 T butter
1/2 cup dry white wine
1 1/4 cup chicken broth
1/2 cup sour cream
1/3 cup grated Parmesan cheese
1 T prepared mustard
Parsley for garnish

2 T olive oil
1 T butter
1 medium onion, diced
2 tsp. chopped fresh tarragon, or 1 tsp. dried
1/2 tsp. fresh thyme, or 1/4 tsp. dried
1 tsp. sea salt
Pepper to taste

In a saucepan, melt the butter. Remove from heat. Stir in the flour. Gradually stir in the wine, chicken broth, and sour cream. Cook over low heat until thickened.

In another saucepan, sauté the onion in olive oil. Add herbs, salt, and pepper and cook just until tender. Add to the thickened sauce and cook 2-3 minutes. Cover cooked chicken with the sauce and bake an additional 15 minutes. Arrange on platter. Garnish with parsley. Use extra sauce as gravy.

Freezing herbs

Many culinary herbs can be snipped, rinsed, dried thoroughly, and then frozen in bags. It works well to freeze dill, sage, rosemary, thyme, tarragon, and stinging nettle on the stem. However, you can also snip the herb off the stem, bag, and freeze.

Chives, oregano, parsley, and lovage are best snipped into small pieces, put into the freezer on a cookie sheet for an hour or so, and then quickly bagged. Either use vacuum bags or remove as much air as possible when bagging.

Another method for use in stews, soups, etc. is to dice the herbs finely (or use a food processor), put into ice cube trays, top with water, and freeze. To preserve freshness, remove the cubes from the tray, put the cubes into a plastic bag, and return to the freezer.

Basil is best frozen by blending and mixing with olive oil, then frozen in ice cube trays, and bagged. Alternatively, make pesto and freeze the pesto.

Teasle, fullers

Dipsacus sativus
Biennial

Teasle helps ease muscular aches and pains such as myalgias and promotes general cleansing of the system. An ointment made from the root is said to be a good wart remedy. Flower heads were once used for raising the nap on woolen cloth.

Teasle is a biennial with a tall rigid stem, growing about four feet high. It bears cylindrical purple flower heads that elongate into a conical shaped seed head with spines. The whole plant is prickly.

Harvest the root in the fall for tincture or decoction. The dried flower head is sometimes used in wild flower arrangements or for craft items.

Thyme

Thymus vulgaris
Half-hardy perennial

Generally considered a culinary herb, thyme is also one of the most medicinal herbs. It strengthens the lungs and helps to open the air pathways, mostly by reducing phlegm, and is reputed to retard the aging process. It is antiviral, antifungal, and expectorant and has been used in the treatment of bronchitis, whooping cough, and other chest infections. It relieves asthmatic type spasms. Thymol, the essential oil in thyme, is strongly antiseptic and is used as a mouthwash and in toothpaste as well as to control varroa mites in honey bees. Thyme tea is excellent during colds and flu. In cooking, it adds a robust savory flavor to fowl, soups, and stews. It is a traditional seasoning, along with sage, for turkey dressing.

The Abbess Hildegard von Bingen said, "He who drinks a cup of thyme tea instead of coffee in the morning will soon feel the beneficial effect: enlivened spirits, great comfort in the stomach, no coughing in the morning and an overall well-being."

There are many varieties of thyme, *Thymus vulgaris* being "common thyme." It is a slow growing short plant with tiny leaves and even tinier flowers, ideal for containers. For harvest the same season, small plants rather than seeds should be planted. Thyme needs full sun and good drainage. Winter wet can cause rot, which causes it to die. To prevent this, put gravel right under the plant and do not mulch, in spite of the fact that severe winters can take their toll. In their native warmer climates in Europe and Asia, thymes grow as perennial shrubs or evergreens.

Congestion reducing tea

2 cups dried thyme
1/2 cup dried meadowsweet flowers
1/2 cup dried elder flowers
1/2 cup lemon balm leaves
1/4 cup dried hyssop—aerial parts

Mix together, breaking up into small pieces.

To infuse: Use 1 teaspoon of the tea blend. Infuse in 1 cup hot, not quite boiling, water for 4 minutes.

If desired, add 1 tsp. honey

Use the leaves, ideally harvested before flowering and picked in the noonday sun, for tisane or tincture. The distilled essential oil is recommended for athlete's foot and scabies, and in aromatherapy for exhaustion, depression, and upper respiratory infections.

Turtlehead

Chelone glabra
Perennial

Turtlehead is a tonic for poor appetite, indigestion, some liver ailments, and general debility. It promotes healthy convalescence from digestive and liver ailments and is mildly anti-depressive. Most frail elderly benefit from the herb. Turtlehead has snapdragon-like white flowers. It grows one and one-half to two feet high, can tolerate wet soil, and does best in partial shade.

Harvest the aerial parts for tisane or tincture, the roots for decoction or tincture.

Valerian

Valeriana officinalis
Perennial

Valerian is a powerful nerve relaxer and antispasmotic that is helpful for back spasm and mental and emotional depression. Mostly noted as a sleep aid, valerian has also been used for St. Vitus dance. It allays pain and promotes sleep while possessing none of the after effects of narcotics. Valerian contains two alkaloids, however, so should not be used regularly or for long periods. It can be combined with skullcap for insomnia caused by depression, and with St. John's wort or hops for anxiety.

An attractive garden plant, native to western Europe, valerian takes a few years to mature. It grows four to five feet high with attractive white flowers in clusters.

Harvest the root in fall for decoction or tincture.

Vervain

Verbena officinalis
Perennial

Historically, vervain was considered an aphrodisiac and associated with sorcerers and witches, giving magical powers to those who used it. It is a nerve tonic, urinary cleanser, and a mild relaxant. Vervain encourages milk flow and promotes effective contractions if taken during labor, although otherwise should be avoided during pregnancy. It combines well with skullcap for depression/anxiety.

Vervain is a perennial that grows up to two feet high. Its flower stalks extend out almost horizontally from the base and its tiny purple flowers are not showy. It grows best in sunny places in well drained soils with frequent rain or watering.

Gather the aerial parts while flowering for tisane or tincture.

Violet, sweet

Viola oderata
Perennial

Syrup of violets is an excellent laxative. *Viola* is also used for sleeplessness and pleurisy. Gerard said that *Viola* "hath the power to ceafe inflammations, roughneff of the throat and comforteth the heart, affwageth paines of the head, and caufeth fleepe..." and also that "There is an oyle made of Violets...being anointed vpon the tefticles doth gently prouoke fleepe which is hindreth by a hot and dry diftemper." The flowers are expectorant and the flower heads can be added to salads or used as a garnish for other dishes. Preparation of the fresh leaves has been used internally and externally in treating cancer, especially cancer of the throat.

Viola oderata is a low growing perennial with rather large heart shaped leaves and small purple flowers not quite an inch in diameter.

A modern method for making syrup of violets is to pound the violets with a mortar, barely cover with water, and steep for two days. Strain. For each pint, add one pound of sugar. Bring just to a boil. Store in the refrigerator. Gerard also described a method for making syrup of violets, which he says is a most perfect purple color. Following are his directions written in modern English: "First, make a clarified syrup by boiling a simple medium syrup, into which put the violet flowers clean picked from all manner of filth, a like quantity as that of the syrup, wherein let them infuse or steep twenty-four hours and set upon a few warm embers; then strain it and put more violets into the same syrup; thus do three or four times, the oftener the better; then set them upon a gentle fire to simmer, but don't boil." He indicated that some add some lemon juice, which improves the beauty, but not the virtue.

Use aerial parts for tisane, tincture, or beautiful syrup. Fresh flowers are edible.

Wild carrot (Queen Anne's lace)

Daucus carota
Biennial

Wild carrot is the ancestor of the common garden carrot. It attracts beneficial insects. The taproot, which is similar in taste to the vegetable carrot but with less flavor, is not as palatable and is much lighter in color, but is edible before the flowers open. It is fine to use in soups and carrot cake. (Be sure you have Queen Anne's Lace, not poison hemlock which looks similar.) The leaves act on the pituitary gland to stimulate sexual hormone production and have a beneficial effect on sexual performance. A decoction of seeds has been used as a traditional hangover cure, probably because of its detoxifying effect. Seeds stimulate the uterus and promote menstruation and have been used as a morning after contraceptive, so should definitely not be taken during pregnancy. *It becomes apparent that this may have been the ancient party herb!* The roots and leaves are used to treat urinary stones and cystitis and help rid the body of uric acid, so are useful in gout. All parts are diuretic.

This is a hardy biennial from which the cultivated carrot was derived. It has fern-like leaves, similar to garden vegetable carrots, and tiny white flowers that form in umbels two to three inches in diameter that eventually form a saucer prior to drying up and closing the seed head. This plant is best suited to a wild flower prairie or a separate garden because it is a prolific self seeder, so is invasive. The roots can be hard to remove, especially in heavy soils. It is beautiful planted in the right place or in a semi-wild area.

Pick the tops of wild carrot after the seed head closes and dries. Use the seed heads for tincture and harvest the root for decoction. To prevent this herb from invading the garden and beyond, remove all of the seed heads.

Wild indigo
Baptisia tinctoria
Half-hardy perennial

Wild indigo is antimicrobial and antiseptic. It is good for persistent infections, especially of the mouth, throat, and respiratory system. It stimulates the immune system and is particularly valuable against bacterial infections. In should be taken in small doses for short periods, since excess may cause nausea and vomiting.

Wild indigo is an attractive garden plant growing one and one-half to two feet high. Purple flowers in spring are borne along an arching raceme, followed by large attractive seed heads. It is native to eastern North America and is somewhat hardy, but can be killed off by a hard winter in zone four.

Harvest the leaves and roots for tincture or decoction.

Wood betony
Stachys officinalis
Perennial

Wood betony is used for headaches and nervous disorders as well as digestive ailments that accompany anxiety. It may be useful for pain in the head and face, such as temporal arteritis, and is a general stimulant and cleanser of the system. It is mildly diuretic and is reputed to have power against evil spirits. Along with hyssop, it has been used to treat epilepsy, which might speak to the historical suggestion of its use against evil spirits that in times past were thought to cause seizures.

Wood betony is a perennial, growing one to two feet high with magenta flowers on spikes.

Harvest aerial parts before and while flowering for tisane or tincture.

Wormwood
Artemisia absinthium
Perennial

The bitterness of wormwood stimulates the liver and gallbladder to digest fats, thus improving appetite and digestion. This very bitter herb is traditionally used in vermouth, absinthe, and other liqueurs and is one of the oldest known remedies for worms, especially roundworms. It has anti-inflammatory effects and acts as a tonic for the liver, digestion, and nerves. Wormwood stimulates the uterus, so should not be used during pregnancy. It should be taken in small doses for only a short time because it contains thujone, which is potentially addicting and in high doses can cause hallucinations.

Wormwood is a sub-shrub with grey-green deeply dissected leaves and insignificant yellow flowers. It grows two to three feet high and is easily cultivated, even in poor soils. It can be invasive, so it is best to isolate the plant. Pruning helps keep it in control. A constituent of the leaves prevents other plants from growing near this herb and is a natural pesticide.

Harvest the aerial parts while in flower for tisane or tincture. The essential oil is not safe for internal use.

Yarrow
Achillea millifolium
Perennial

This herb was named after Achilles who used yarrow to heal injuries in battle. It has also been used in divination. Yarrow stalks were traditionally cast when consulting the *I Ching,* the Chinese ancient book of divination. It is also said that putting a sprig of yarrow under a pillow will reveal a future husband or wife. Yarrow reputedly helps keep negative energy from those around you from affecting you. It is often called soldiers' herb or carpenters' weed because of its use to stop bleeding and heal wounds, and perhaps because of its reputed use for gonorrhea. To stop bleeding, crush or chew the leaves and apply fresh to a wound. When taken internally, yarrow lowers fever, helps prevent thrombosis after a heart attack or stroke, and helps prevent hemorrhage. In addition, it is used for uterine fibroids, blood filled cysts, blood clots, and varicose veins. The flowers diminish various allergic problems such as hay fever. An essential oil made from yarrow is an anti-inflammatory. Large doses should be avoided during pregnancy.

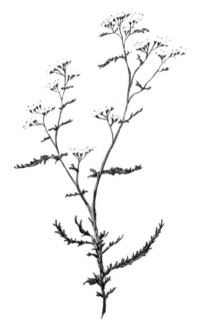

Gerard said, "The leaues of Yarrow do clofe vp wounds and keepe them from inflammation or fiery fwellings; it ftancheth bloud in any part of the body and is likewife put into baths for women to fit in; it stoppeth the laske and being drunke it helpeth the bloudy flixe." He adds, "It cureth the inward excorations of the yard of a man, comming by reafon of pollutions or extreme flowing of the feed (seed), although the iffue do caufe inflammation and fwelling of thofe fecret parts, and though the fpermatic matter do come downe in great quantity, if the juice be injected with a fyringe or the decoction." He wrote that a friend of his had proved this many times using it on himself and his fellows when he was a student in Cambridge and a single fellow.

Treben noted that the Abbe Kniepp wrote, "Women could be spared many troubles if they just took yarrow tea from time to time be it a young girl with irregular menses or an older woman during menopause."

An aromatic perennial with a very distinctive odor, wild yarrow is white and grows to about one foot high in most soils. Cultivated yarrow is less invasive than the wild and is a good border plant, often having purple to red or pink flowers. Its bloom attract beneficial insects.

Harvest the flowers for most uses and the leaves to stop bleeding. Use fresh flowers in infusions and to breathe in its hot steam for asthma and allergies. Use aerial parts as an infusion for yarrow's anti-inflammatory and fever-reducing qualities. The essential oil of yarrow is good for massages as well as for chest rubs during a cold or flu. Dried aerial parts reduce fever, stimulate circulation, and reduce blood pressure. Combined with goldenseal and ground together, dried yarrow flowers make an excellent first aid powder.

The Sherman Tomb

My travel is limited, in part because the beauty of my prairie home can rarely be equaled, and the solace I find at Animal Farm can't be surpassed. I also abhor tourist traps and the sameness of restaurants and shopping sites in most such locales. However, occasionally the promise of an interesting journey lures me away from my home.

It was the hat I first noticed when I jerked my head up, startled by the sharply spoken words, "What exactly are you doing?"

The hat was black with a wide round brim. The face below it was stern. The man had a thin, angular face and wore a long black robe. His eyes looked black, as well.

Alice, my mother-in-law, standing on the ground next to me started sputtering, "Uh..uh...it's my family's tomb. Ah... She was trying to read the words on it."

I was on my knees on top of a large marble and brick above-ground crypt which stood near the entrance to the Parish Church of St. Mary the Virgin in Dedham, England. I climbed onto it to try to make out the names of the persons buried within and the story it told. When positioned that way, the filtered sunlight shining directly on the marble allowed me to see the grime-filled etching well enough to run my finger over the letters. I had deciphered some of the words etched two and a half centuries earlier.

I scrambled off the crypt with a feeling of shame similar to when my dad caught me smoking when I was twelve-years-old. I began explaining in a small voice, "I'm sorry. I couldn't read the letters without being on top of it. We were told the tomb contains the remains of her family." I motioned to my mother-in-law. "Most of the Shermans left here by 1649 and came to America," I said with a little stronger voice, "and my mother-in-law here is a Sherman."

The vicar's rigid stance and implacable expression didn't change. "We try to keep the little children off the gravestones," he said in a scolding voice.

"We know about the Sherman family," he continued. "See that window at the end of the church?" He pointed to a stained glass window some forty or fifty feet high. "The family donated the funds for that window in the 1600s."

"If you want more information, come back to the church at five o'clock. We have a book containing the genealogy of the Sherman family. I believe you'll find the words taken from this tomb in that manuscript."

He nodded then, and a glimmer of kindness crept into his eyes, which I could then see were a deep blue. He began to walk away, then turned and added, "You must stay in the church while looking at the book."

I watched the vicar walk toward the church; then I looked at Alice. I wasn't sure what to expect from this retired school teacher from Casper, Wyoming. She was the sort of woman who followed rules to the letter and I feared she'd be angry with me for causing a scene. "How embarrassing," she said, but she was smiling.

I chuckled a little then, relieved from the presence of the imposing vicar and glad for Alice's smile. We both began giggling. "I think we need an ale before we return at five," I said, and we set off to find a pub.

A Practice in Serenity

Some people meditate. Some read their Bibles or their Korans. Some people chant. Others sit quietly in a boat, whether fishing or not, and open themselves to a spiritual connection.

I weed.

When I don old jeans, a hat, and some gloves to begin weeding one of my nine gardens, the task seems formidable. Early in the season, weeding requires gentle prodding around the tiny vegetables and herbs. Care is needed to distinguish a young onion from a blade of grass. As the season develops, I clearly see the rows of produce. I also see the rows between them, green with crabgrass, a little clover, a stalk or two of pigweed, a few dandelions, and the tiny box elder "trees" that have found a home in the once black soil. When I return a couple of weeks after the previous weeding, quack grass with its long rhizome has often again encroached into the garden.

I begin. Bending down, I start my vigil on hands and knees. The hand-weeder in my right hand dislodges the roots while my left hand grabs the uprooted crabgrass or clover. With hands working in rhythmic unison, soon a stretch of garden is once again black and beautiful. The weeding begun, the process settles into routine. One row clean of weeds, then two.

My mind wanders as I weed. I plan an event. I remember a call I forgot to make. At ease in the garden, I often think about my work as a guardian ad litem for the Court where I work with children whose lives have been disrupted by their parents' divorce or neglect or abuse. The recommendations I am called upon to make are often heart-wrenching and I struggle to decide what makes sense. Sometimes as I weed, clarity comes, a direction forms. It is as if the ground itself conveys wisdom. Sometimes I lose myself as the minutes pass and several feet of ground are cleared. I enter a state of mind—not thinking, not evaluating, not organizing. I'm simply there in the garden, tuning in to the plants or to a natural connection with nature.

For most of us, including me, it is easy to measure our worth by the amount of work we do, the money we make, and the praise (or not) of bosses and customers. And yet, how shallow a life such an orientation creates. We all must do some work, of course. As we use resources, so must we contribute to the creation of them. As we use services, so must we contribute our own service. When our work flows from who we are, it nourishes the soul. But, when work is emphasized to the occlusion of other important things in our life, we may lose our sense of being connected to something larger than ourselves and lose our own souls in the process.

Weeding helps me to know that I am a part of this amazing process of life.

I must also admit that I am sometimes miserable out there in the garden. When the thermometer rises above ninety and the dew point reaches seventy, and the sweat pours off, I feel wretched. But even then, I find that after a short time on my hands and knees, my body adjusts and the misery diminishes. When mosquitoes are plentiful, I want to scream—and sometimes do. I don't use chemical mosquito repellants, so when the sceeters are really bad I put on my Bug Baffler, a tight mesh jacket that also covers my head and face. I sweat more, but I don't go completely buggy.

You may wonder why I don't hoe more and hand-weed less. My husband wonders, too. I don't know whether I am poor at hoeing or if I have too many weeds that are tough to hoe. With many of my crops, the weeds snuggle in next to the small vegetables and herbs, too close to hoe without damaging the plants. Hand weeding helps me pay more attention to insect problems in the garden and to notice the slugs, worms, and toads in the soil. I guess I just prefer to hand-weed.

Give me a seventy degree day with a few clouds in the sky, a mild breeze keeping the mosquitoes at bay and a damp, but not wet, garden and weeding becomes serene—at least until my wrists begin aching or my feet start going to sleep from "praying" too long.

Seeds ... Life Ready to Spring Forth

A tiny carrot seed, a tomato seed just larger than a pinhead, a kernel of popcorn, a potato from last fall's harvest.... They don't look alive, and yet, add some soil and water and life springs forth.

A few years ago I ordered some Japanese yellow hull-less popcorn seed, planted it and produced an abundant crop of great popcorn, enough to satisfy John's love affair—with the popcorn and maybe with me for growing it—for a couple of years. Last year, I could only find Japanese *white* hull-less popcorn. It was good, but the kernels were a little smaller and were not as beautiful as the shiny yellow-gold of its sibling.

I searched seed catalogs and the internet for Japanese *yellow* hull-less popcorn. No luck. Then I noticed that we still had a couple of cups of the yellow popcorn in a jar. So, in February I planted twelve seeds to see if they would germinate. Ten of the seeds sent up a green shoot, demonstrating that they lived. When they were a couple of inches high, I put them outside in the sun for the brief period they could survive in the cold. Just a little time in the sun seemed better than none. They had lived as seeds for about three years. Since it was much too early to plant them in the garden, they would have only a couple of weeks of opening to the world and I felt sad at their premature death.

Assuming the beautiful yellow popcorn seeds were open pollinated, like the white, I planted them when the soil warmed. In the dark soil, their DNA knew what to do. Soon, a green shoot pushed through into the light. The plant climbed. It tasseled creating seeds and silky threads of womb. A cob of corn formed.

I'll harvest the popcorn and again in a year or two, I'll plant some of those seeds to carry on the life contained within them. Most of the seeds, of course, will be popped, ending their living DNA potential. When I think much about it, I feel sad about that ending. Yet, through human manipulation and planting, many more maize seeds—whether popcorn or field corn or sweet corn—will have their time in the sun than they would have had, were it not for human cultivation. It is, after all, a reciprocal relationship.

A Solomon seal berry may be plucked by a bird from one garden, eaten by the bird, become feces, and fall into a different garden to root and flourish. A garden mallow seed may lay dormant in the ground for decades, waiting its turn to feel the sun and the rain. Seeds develop within an apple, all carrying genes unlike their parents or siblings and perhaps more like a distant ancestor in Kazakhstan. The remarkable odyssey of each of these seeds brings the word "miraculous" to mind.

When I plant pepper seeds, celery, tomatoes, foxglove, and Joe Pye weed, I feel a deep honor for the tiny packages of life that were harvested at a nursery far away, waited in the seed packet, and are finally ready to express their destiny using the soil and water I give them.

Monsanto and other multinational corporations ignore that honor. Through their engineering, their patents, and their increasing control of the global food market, they thwart not only nature, but small farmers around the world. The pervasive philosophy of these corporate giants invades our entire culture, diminishing our respect for the vital nature of seeds and the inherent value of life's diversity.

Each Season has its Pleasures

As the sun moved toward the southwestern horizon on a sunny day in mid-November, John and I sat on our deck. I felt aglow, not only from the fragrant Merlot I sipped, but from the mood of the day. The sun warmed, but didn't heat. The dry leaves lazily tumbled on the grass that was still bright with the vibrant green reminiscent of spring. The vegetable gardens were tilled in readiness for a new planting season months away, while the herb gardens were still alive with brilliant parsley and self seeded cilantro, along with frost-dulled sage and thyme.

As the sun retreated from the southwestern sky, it created a soft and quiet mood. Perhaps I felt pensive, knowing these warm days were ending, that soon snow would snuff out the remnants of summer. But, I was not sad, for each season has its wonders and its pleasures.

Two days later, I drove east on Highway 9 through a gentle mid-afternoon rain. Glancing to the north, I noticed a rainbow. The primary rainbow arched from horizon to horizon. Above it, in subtler tones, the light reflected a second rainbow. This gift of nature quieted the anxiousness I felt on the day of yet further violence in the Middle East. Rainbows always herald hope and that day's rainbow was so rich with color that it filled me with a sense of peace.

Soon snow would fly. John and I would sip our morning coffee while the warm radiance from the fiery dance in the wood heating stove warmed our skin. I would appreciate that ambiance as much as that of the sunny November afternoon and the day the rainbow looked down upon me. Another winter day I'd make lefse on the wood cook stove and bake some oatmeal bread and the smell of fresh bread would permeate our home.

In February, the seed catalogs would be laid out on the table and I'd again begin dreaming of the day when garlic stalks would push through the mulch and the tiny leaves of sweet corn would enter the light of the day.

The season would turn again and harvest time would come.

Each season reflects a different face of nature, offering its range of hues, its gifts of color. Each season brings new challenges, new memories, and renewed beauty .

The Swallows Dance

The swallows again built a mud nest above our kitchen window. This was the third season they had returned to that spot. *Are they the same swallows each year?* I wondered. *Do they, like the salmon and the trumpeter swan, return to their birth place to nest year after year?*

The first year they came, I used a hose to try to squirt down their partially built nest, preferring that the swallows find a place where their droppings were less noticeable. Two times I knocked down the nest and two times the swallows found more building material and re-weaved their nest. Their persistence won out and I decided to be a good neighbor to these graceful birds with sleek bodies, iridescent blue backs, and golden-orange underbellies.

Time passed. The nest was too high for me to easily see the eggs, but I knew they were there. Soon I heard the soft cries of nestlings waiting for the return of a parent and some tasty mosquitoes or flies.

My husband John and I returned home one evening to find five tiny swallows on the deck beneath the window. As we approached, a couple of them scooted away, falling off the deck to the ground below. John scooped the nestlings up and put them back into a crowded nest.

The next morning, five tiny birds again were flailing around on the deck. *Were there too many? Were these the weaker of the flock and simply being discarded?* Again John returned the birds to the overflowing nest. But, within hours several of the tiny birds were back on the deck.

We barricaded the east side of the deck, preventing our dogs from investigating the interesting creatures. For two or three weeks we observed the parents' ritual of seeking food, returning with food in their mouths to feed the "deck brood," then flying off again to return a little later to feed the babies in the nest.

John and I began a morning and evening ritual of watching these young birds and noting their growth, hoping they would survive until they could fly.

Soon one of the nestlings became a fledgling. Not quite as graceful as its parent, the young swallow nonetheless was agile and fluid in flight. John and I were almost as excited as when our children had taken their first steps. Within days, all of the young were swooping and soaring with their parents.

Fall approached and we knew it would soon be time for the swallows to head south, flying up to five hundred miles a day. As I sat at the kitchen table watching one of the last-of-the-season graceful flights of the swallow family, a hawk darted across the sky and grabbed one of the young. Such occurrences must happen almost daily on our five acres, but this one happened to a young bird I knew, who I had helped to survive. I wiped away a tear trickling down my cheek, then another.

By a week later I no longer heard the twitterings of the family, and I knew they were on their way to Mexico or Costa Rica or Argentina.

It was a sunny day early the next May. I sat at the kitchen table, sipping steaming coffee, surveying the newly tilled gardens.

Within minutes a dozen swallows appeared in formation above the lush park-like grass out beyond the gardens. Diving and gliding and soaring and swooping in

117

choreographed synchronization, they entranced me in their dance. *Was it fifteen minutes? Had an hour passed while I watched?* I felt giddy, enraptured by their beauty and their grace.

I had a sense that these swallows were dancing for me, that they created this beauty to communicate to John and me their appreciation for helping them survive to fly another season.

Soon, with nesting material in their mouths, a pair of swallows began building a nest above our kitchen window for another summer's hatch. I hoped the nest would be large enough to hold all of the young.

Mama Grosbeak Attends Death

Thunk!

I knew the sound. A bird had flown into the window. This time it didn't just graze the window. It hit hard.

I didn't want to look, but knew I must. There on the ground lay a female rose-breasted grosbeak. "Oh, no," I said aloud, although only the cats and dogs could hear. I checked to see if our three cats were in the house. Closing the door to keep the cats from exiting through the animal door used by our pets, I hurried outside.

I approached the bird, assuming it was the female grosbeak we had often seen at the feeder. Kneeling down, I cupped my hands toward it, thinking to bring it to higher ground to keep it from cats, whether it were dead or alive. I could see it still lived as I drew near.

My hands were just about to touch the bird when I saw another female grosbeak on the ground watching from less than a foot away. With her brown stripes, she had blended into the background as my attention was drawn to the bird who had hit the window. The nearly dead bird flapped its wings a bit and moved closer to the bird who I somehow knew could only be Mama Grosbeak. I stood up and backed away as Mama nestled the bird under her wing.

The mother bird had not flown when I approached.

Maternal instinct? A sense of duty? Maternal care? Could it be love? She must have been frightened when I drew near, but she did not fly.

As I walked away, I could see the injured bird's neck was twisted. I knew it would not survive. From inside the house I watched as she died in the embrace of her mother. Mama stayed a few minutes after the death, and then she flew.

I rubbed the moistness from my eyes, found some nesting material that had fallen to the ground from another bird, and made a small nest in a space formed by a broken branch on a box elder tree.

I gathered the dead young grosbeak and gently placed her in the nest. Her grave should be in a tree, not on the ground where dogs and cats and squirrels would sniff or eat.

Death and decay happen all around me in the natural world. Ants, bees, mice, raccoons die without my notice. Yet, those deaths I witness bring sadness and sometimes tears.

Mama Grosbeak did not return to the feeder in the following days. Whether she moved on or simply stayed away from the feeder and window, I don't know. I missed her and her brood.

My husband John and I watch many birds come to the feeder. We struggle with the reality that each year a few of these birds are victims of our cats or our windows. We gave away a cat we dearly loved, the cat we believed to be the smartest of our felines. She was also the best hunter and seemed to have a greater instinct to attack and kill than our other cats. Mice, striped gophers, birds—they were all fair game to her. We couldn't stand to watch—or to know. The three cats we still feed and house often have mouse dinner, but rarely kill a bird. I'm not sure how I justify the hierarchy that allows me to see a dead mouse without feeling a loss, but can't do the same if the death is that of a gopher or a bird.

Earlier that summer, one of our cats did catch a bird—a male Baltimore oriole. He, too, had been a regular visitor to our feeder. John and I called him Paul Neumann because he was so beautiful. When the cat ran into the house with bird in mouth, John screamed. The cat dropped the bird. Paul darted up and flew into a window and knocked himself out. While I cornered the cat, John picked up the oriole. He went out onto the deck, with me following, cradling the bird in his hands. The bird's feet grasped John's finger, a good sign. His eyes flickered and he looked around. John occasionally opened his hands to see if the bird would fly. About fifteen minutes after leaving the mouth of the cat, Paul Neumann made his escape to the trees.

I saw him flying the next day and smiled for his life.

Darkness—A Solstice Tradition

In years past, the longest night of the year was experienced in darkness, save for moonlight and star-studded skies. Ancient societies honored this long, dark night and, in ceremony, welcomed the turning toward spring.

As societies developed the technologies of candles and torches, and later gas or kerosene lanterns, they began to lose that sense of dark and shadow. Then came electricity and our experience of the night waned even more. No longer did mankind use stars for navigation and the moon to reckon time. Dawn and dusk no longer defined the waking hours. Communities no longer commemorated the solstice with song and dance. Television watching and internet surfing replaced contemplation of the constellations. Light pollution clouded the once spectacular diamonds in a velvet sky.

John and I have our own solstice tradition. From the time of arising on the winter solstice until we arise the next morning, we use no electric lights. Our wood burning stove casts radiant heat and gentle light. We burn candles that cast dancing shadows in their flickering glow. As evening approaches, the dark envelopes us, and the preparation of dinner is complicated by the lack of bright lights. Even pouring coffee or milk is more difficult than it might seem. The dinner itself, however, is romantic and mysterious.

Our bedtime usually comes early on the evening of the solstice. After reading by candlelight has strained our eyes and watching the clouds pass in front of the moon no longer holds our attention, we retire. But, once again, we remember a time long ago and awaken the next morning with more appreciation for Thomas Edison's invention as well as for our ancestors who sang and chanted in honor of the darkness and in anticipation of the light to come.

I wonder to what extent our lighted cultures have lost a sense of wonder, of awe, a grasp of the mysterious. Are our modern addictions to chemicals, to work, to money, and to material stuff a striving toward something that can only be found in the dark?

A Sparrow Survives

Dark still enveloped the outside world early on a winter morning, although a hint of light was visible in the southeast. I'd given basset hound Lady a little lovin' and had put out food for the three cats. Only two cats had come for their morning fare of Fancy Feast cat food. I was wondering where Elvira was when she came dashing down from upstairs. I figured she was heading for her food, but she didn't go to the food. I looked closer and then yelled to John who was closer to her, "She's got something. Grab her."

John grabbed Elvira, forcing her to drop a little sparrow. I grabbed Dosie, a feral cat that has lived with us for six years or so, but was still leery of touching contact with us humans. Putz, a golden tabby was feeding below a large window when the sparrow flew toward the window, bounced off, and landed near the cat. Putz grabbed the bird. I shrieked. A terrified Dosie clawed me, forcing me to drop her. She ran upstairs to hide while I grabbed Elvira, threw her into a room and closed the door while John grabbed Putz, who let the sparrow go. The bird flew behind the piano, a safer place than she'd been for several moments.

Eventually John and I forced the sparrow out from behind the piano. Cradling her in my hands, I took her outside and placed her atop a woodpile in the protected wood shed. She didn't fly right away, but she was alive. I don't know if she survived, but I hope she did.

It's easy to wonder if the sparrow was grateful to have survived the jaws of two cats, a bump on a window, and being grabbed by two big hands. But, likely she was in shock and, if she eventually flew, simply went on with life with no thought about her near death experience.

We've had birds in our house before. A cat has occasionally brought one in through the pet entrance during the warmer seasons when the inside door is open. We've had birds come down our chimney, then let them into the house by leaving the door to the stove open. Eventually the birds have either flown out an open door, or John or I have captured them and brought them outside to complete their escape. But on the winter morning described above, Elvira had clearly grabbed the sparrow outside and brought her indoors through the access the cats have discovered into our attic.

John and I have looked for the access route in the attic but have never found it. The first time we became aware of it, we heard knocking coming from the inside of the attic door near our bed. We discovered Putz inside the attic. He'd been banging on the door to be let in. Once we recognized he could come and go that way, we left the attic door open. All of the cats we've had over the years since then have learned the route, except for Dosie who has never liked to climb. The access allows the cats to come and go as they please whether we are home or not and, except for Dosie, relieves us of the "let the cats out, let the cats in" routine we'd become accustomed to. I've worried that squirrels would find the entry way, but we've had no squirrels or other animal visitors, apart from a few mice the cats usually find before we do.

Although I cope with the cats killing mice much easier than I do with their destruction of birds, I have occasionally forced a cat to drop a mouse when the cat and mouse game goes on too long. Even though I don't like mice in the house, I manage their presence better than I do watching their torture.

Knowledge in Nature

The indigo bunting visits the birdfeeder, followed by a male goldfinch. The contrasting iridescence of the blue and the brightness of the yellow rivets my attention. Another day a male and female orchard oriole visit while a humming bird hovers at the nearby feeder.

The mint reigns royal in the herb garden with the mother of thyme creating circular mounds while the rows of basil slowly develop fullness as the plants inch their way toward more sunlight.

Ash trees and box elders add feet to their overhang each year, requiring more pruning than I find time to complete. A maple tree, only five or six years old, pushes its way toward thirty feet in the air as its feet find nourishment in the fertile soil.

These visions are part of my everyday summer existence. They occur in the city, too, but in the country, devoid of many artificial intrusions, their daily miracles soothe my soul and deepen my appreciation for the interconnectedness of all life forms.

My radio, most often tuned to Minnesota Public Radio, brings stories of global warming, spiraling gasoline prices, suicide bombers, and health care costs. Along with war, finance and fiduciary concerns dominate the news. Our political leaders, whether conservative or liberal, focus heavily on economic prosperity and the resulting control of the world market and the power that such control buys.

Most of us follow the golden or green-backed paper Pied Piper and it is hard to argue against prosperity. But, my soul beckons for me to pay more attention to the rose-breasted grosbeak and the lavender in bloom. The quest for material objects seems to be an artificial and short-lived quench to the thirst for that spiritual knowledge that nature provides. It is a knowledge that deepens when the quiet is broken only by a robin's song, when the scent of chamomile hangs heavy after a summer rain, or by the vision of a rainbow arched against a tallgrass prairie.

A Winter Sunrise

The four of us conversed easily as we sipped Just Coffee, a fair trade brand. John and I had been invited to view an early January sunrise and then have breakfast with Don and Helen. Their house, which was built primarily with their own four hands, nestles into a hillside. The living room windows, with a southeast exposure, sit some twelve feet above the ground. They overlook acres of virgin rolling prairie designed by glaciers and their aftermath millennia ago.

As we watched through the window, a layer of rose formed just over the horizon beneath a bank of grey clouds. Then wisps of pink developed in the feathery higher clouds, creating a vision one expects to see captured by artists. Within minutes the window was filled with striations and puffs and swirls of pink in the filmy grey upper clouds, while the earth's rotation toward the sun painted the sky just above the horizon a deep pinkish-orange. As the dawn came, black angus cattle began ambling over the rise, moving toward the house in the slow rhythm of nature. Our conversation stopped as we watched, the scene suggesting the serenity of quiet solitude. The room brightened while the four of us remained silently watching.

Spring Comes with Autumn's Perspective

Spring emerges with the stinging nettle birthing its maroon-tinged leaves through the black soil, offering energy and healing to our wintered bodies. Soon newly planted blades of grass show green, buds blossom pink on the apple trees, and the dandelion's bloom draws the honey bees.

I remember the spring of my life, or some of it: being bounced on Grandpa's knee, tasting a fresh strawberry, swinging as high as my pumping legs would carry me, and playing dress-up with my grandma's old clothes.

It was in the spring, too, when I studied hard in high school, when I decided to become a nurse, graduated from college, married and had a child. Spring was turning toward summer as I cradled newborn Greg in my arms and nursed him at my breast. I watched as his small arms stretched high to plink the piano. At work on the pediatric station I used silver nitrate solution as I wrapped little Jimmy's body that was covered with the blisters of epidermolysis bullosa and provided what comfort I could as Susan succumbed to cystic fibrosis.

In summertime, the cucumbers mature, rosemary develops pungency, the flavor of the garlic intensifies, and apples enlarge and develop a rosy tinge.

And in the summer of my life, I divorced, remarried, and became a mom to Johnny and Misty. My home hours were busy with household tasks, nurturing children, tending a small garden, and cooking nutritious meals not always appreciated by the children. At work as a public health nurse, I helped new moms learn how to care for their babies and assisted the frail elderly as they moved from independence to dependence. Later, jointly publishing a newspaper with John, working life diverted attention from the needs of our children.

As life's summer began to fade, John and I found a home in the country. We found strength in the earth, her creatures, and her plants. We held our son, JW, as he succumbed to lung failure two years after a heart and lung transplant. We encouraged Greg as he honed his musical talent. We coped with Misty's pain, supported her in recovery, and watched her blossoming into her own summer. Later, I watched my mom's breaths slow, giving way to the toxicity of kidney failure and sang a hymn to my dad as an old-age heart attack ceased the beating of his heart and opened him to a journey of which I know not.

The fall of the year has always my favorite season. The vibrant green of summer's maples gives way to the beauty of amber, orange, and brown. The corn stalks lose their chlorophyll and become brittle while the sage leaves retain their green well past the early frosts.

Life's autumn has begun and informs my thoughts of spring. Seedlings rise toward the grow lights in the house. Potato seeds send out shoots beneath the soil. I prepare to plant thyme, rosemary, tomatoes, and squash. I'll look forward to harvesting tarragon in June and apples in October. Yet, lacking the intense energy of spring and summer, my life is quieter and a little slower. My eyesight dims, my hearing fades; yet, perhaps these failings heighten discernment and philosophic thought.

My country, too, having experienced spring and summer, is now in its fall. Its movement toward winter seems less reflective than my own, less open to the wisdom that age can bring. Its policies yield resource destruction. It has forgotten that it was founded upon religious tolerance, not on proselytizing and using bombs to spread the word. In large measure my society has forgotten the slow quietness required to nurture the spirits of our children. My fellow citizens have too often been persuaded that greed is good and that consumerism is the solution to society's ills. Forgetting responsibilities to each other and to our grandchildren, we allow the earth to be raped for today's gains and contribute to the debt of our children, and theirs.

Perhaps these thoughts spring from sage wisdom that blooms during the autumn years. Or perhaps a denied longing for a spring long past paints the clouds darker than the reality.

Either way, spring brings renewed strength and a positive outlook. Aili, my granddaughter, regularly reminds me of the excitement this season calls forth. A stinging nettle casserole will provide nourishment for spring's work. While pulling weeds and mowing grass, I'll continue to reflect and to open myself to the beauty of my surroundings. I'll mulch a sage leaf to incorporate its wisdom to feed the thoughts of an autumn mind. And I'll continue to write about some of those perceptions as autumn's rich hues develop.

SOURCES

Bown, Deni. *Herbal; The Essential Guide to Herbs for Living.* New York: Barnes and Noble Books, 2001.

Cupleper, Nicholas. *Culpeper's English Physician and Complete Herbal*, arranged as an herbal by Mrs. C. F. Leyel. No. Hollywood, CA: Wilshire Book Company, 1972.

Dr. Nicholas Culpeper lived and wrote in the seventeenth century. *Culpeper's English Physician and Complete Herbal, Enlarged* was published in 1652.

Gerard, John. *The Herbal or General History of Plants*, a replication of The Complete 1633 Edition as revised and enlarged by Thomas Johnson. New York: Dover Publications, Inc., 1975.

Herbal Society of America, The. *New Encyclopedia of Herbs and Their Uses.* London, New York, Munich, Melbourne, Delhi: Dorling Kindersley, Revised edition, 2001.

Ody, Penelope. *The Complete Medicinal Herbal.* London, New York, Stuttgart: Dorling Kindersley, 1st American edition, 1993.

Treben, Marie. *Health Through God's Pharmacy.* Steyr, Austria: Publisher Ennsthaler, 26th edition, 1998.

Wood, Matthew. *The Book of Herbal Wisdom.* Berkeley, CA: North Atlantic Books, 1997.

In addition to using this book as source, information learned directly through Wood's classes is incorporated into the author's thinking and throughout the manuscript.

GLOSSARY

Adaptogen   That which is cleansing, stimulating effective removal of waste products, and which has a balancing effect on the whole body.

Antioxidant   Molecules found in plants and animals that prevent oxidation of other chemicals and therefore may diminish breakdown in cells and resultant pathology.

Antitussive   Inhibiting the cough reflex, thus reducing coughing.

Decoction   A remedy made by boiling barks, twigs, berries, and roots in water, a method that extracts more vigorously than simply soaking in hot water.

Diaphoretic   Assisting in opening the pores of the skin and therefore causing sweating and reducing fever.

Emetic   Stimulating vomiting.

Infusion   An herb soaked in hot water, then used hot as a tisane or cold; or soaked in oil, then heated on the stove or placed in the sun, for use as a massage oil, cream, or ointment.

Laxative   Encouraging bowel movements.

Nervine   That which affects the nervous system in a healthy fashion, whether stimulating, relaxing, or sedating.

Poultice   An application of fresh or dried herbs directly to the skin, usually applied hot, having been soaked in boiling water.

Purgative   Severely laxative.

Tincture   An herbal extract made by soaking fresh herbs, whether aerial parts, roots or barks, in an alcohol such as vodka, rum, or brandy.

Tisane   An herbal infusion, often called a tea, made by soaking aerial parts of an herb in hot water just off the boil, then steeping for a few minutes.

Tonic   Restoring, nourishing, and supporting the entire body.

INDEX

INDEX

INDEX

INDEX

INDEX